# Christmas

Published by Scholastic Publications Ltd,
Villiers House,
Clarendon Avenue,
Leamington Spa,
Warwickshire CV32 5PR

**Compiler** Pat Gooch
**Editor** Juliet Gladston
**Series designer** Joy White
**Designer** Elizabeth Harrison
**Cover Illustration & illustrations** Val Biro

Designed using Aldus Pagemaker
Processed by Salvo Design and Print, Leamington Spa
Artwork by David Harban Design, Warwick
Printed in Great Britain by Ebenezer Baylis & Son Ltd,
Worcester

**British Library Cataloguing-in-Publication Data**
A catalogue record for this book is
available from the British Library.

ISBN 0-590-53025-9

# Contents

## POETRY

## STORIES



## PLAYS

# SONGS



# GAMES

# THINGS TO MAKE

# POETRY

## Christmas

Christmas comes but once a year.
Nuts and crackers, crisps and beer.

Christmas isn't inexpensive
Shopping trips are most extensive.

What would every Christmas be
without a tinselled Christmas tree?

Who could get to sleep at nights
without a string of fairy lights?

The whole thing would not work at all
if cards weren't covering the wall.

We'd think there'd been a slight mishap
without the presents to unwrap.

The dinner mood would get quite murky
if there was Spam instead of turkey.

Festivities would seem a hoax
without the cracker's corny jokes.

It's odd how all these customs stem
from one far night in Bethlehem.

Charles Thomson

# Once there was a shepherd

Once there was a shepherd on a dark hill
and he saw a light.
The light shone deep into the cave of his mind
and before he went to bed
he phoned his neighbour:
'I'm still angry about that fence
but I saw a light on Garn Fadryn Hill'.
Soon all the wires were baa-ing with voices saying
'Ewan Evans has seen a light!'

The farmer and his neighbour couldn't sleep
so, after meeting at the end of the Drift,
they walked down the High Street
past the video shop, the chippie, the Sonar Bangla,
the baker's, the chemist's and Mrs Bowman's –
picking up wanderers on the way –
lovers in doorways, a tramp with his Happy Shopper bag.
They came to The King of Glory.
It was packed with visitors from the city:
drunks singing in hope of a better day tomorrow,
quiet men and women gazing into the distance.
A boy and a girl leaned in the doorway with Colas.
In one corner a man in a suit counted his money.
The landlord and his wife were sweating and red.
Ewan's neighbour whispered:
'Ewan Evans has seen a light!'

They went round the back.
The crowd got bigger and bigger.
They passed the toilets, squeezed down a smoky corridor
out into a yard of crates, bottles and cracked flagstones.
A cat crept by on some sharp catty task. Dogs yapped.
Sheep had broken through a decrepit fence
and were sucking a patch of grass by the pub wall.
Only Ewan was certain for going on.
His companions were scared of the dark
and light that crossed the hill
like a huge luminous asterisk –
but in the garage they saw a family.
'Ewan Evans has seen a light!'

Like a perfect verse in three lines,
bread fresh on your tongue –
Mary, and Joseph, and the babe lying in a manger....
They smiled on the shepherd and his friends
who knelt, and forgot their fences.

Fred Sedgwick

## The cook sees the stable

He sees the straw on the floor like
spaghetti on a plate, without bolognese.
The smell of the stable
reminds him of mustard.
The animals are standing still.
He has a vision of cooking beef.
The cradle looks like a lump of meat loaf.
Jesus is crying
as though he wants some milk.
Mary is sweet as the sugar we put in the tea.
The shepherd's gifts
look like big fruit cakes.
Joseph smells
like warm mince pies
being eaten on Christmas Day.

Katie Eastman, aged 10

# Christmas Eve

I'm trying to sleep on Christmas Eve
but I really can't settle down,
and I don't want to lie
with wide open eyes
till the morning comes around.

I hear Mum and Dad downstairs,
doing their best to keep quiet,
and although I'm tucked in,
covers up to my chin,
in my head there's a terrible riot.

I'm thinking of Christmas morning
and all the presents I'll find,
but what if I've missed
something good off my list,
it keeps going round in my mind.

Mum has been baking all day
making rolls, mince pies and cake,
and I know quite well
it's this heavenly smell
that's keeping me wide awake.

Perhaps I'll slip down for some water
though I ought to stay in my room,
but maybe I'll risk
a slap with the whisk
for a lick of Mum's mixing spoon.

If I had just one mince pie
then I know it would be alright,
fast asleep,
not another peep,
my eyes shut tightly all night.

Now Dad says Father Christmas
won't leave any presents for me,
*Make no mistake,*
*if you're still awake,*
*he'll pass you by, you'll see!*

But I've tried and I've tried and I've tried
and I keep rolling round in my bed,
I still can't sleep,
and I'm fed up with sheep
so I'm counting reindeer instead!

Brian Moses

# Tidy up for Christmas

| | |
|---|---|
| I want this house tidied up for Christmas, | *Wag finger.* |
| So everybody help and we'll soon get it done. | *Wag finger at everyone.* |
| I'll wash the dishes. | *Pretend to wash dishes.* |
| You dry the dishes. | *Pretend to wipe dishes.* |
| I'm not wiping dishes that's no fun! | *Put hands on hips in protest.* |
| | |
| I want this house tidied up for Christmas, | *Wag finger.* |
| So everybody help and we'll soon get it done. | *Wag finger at everyone.* |
| I'll sweep the floor. | *Pretend to sweep the floor.* |
| You wash the floor. | *Pretend to scrub the floor.* |
| I'm not washing floors that's no fun! | *Put hands on hips in protest.* |
| | |
| I want this house tidied up for Christmas, | *Wag finger.* |
| So everybody help and we'll soon get it done. | *Wag finger at everyone.* |
| I'll do the hoovering. | *Pretend to hoover the floor.* |
| You do the dusting. | *Pretend to dust.* |
| I'm not doing dusting that's no fun! | *Put hands on hips in protest.* |
| | |
| I want this house tidied up for Christmas, | *Wag finger.* |
| So everybody help and we'll soon get it done. | *Wag finger at everyone.* |
| I'll make the cake. | *Pretend to stir a cake.* |
| You ice the cake. | *Pretend to ice a cake.* |
| I'll eat the cake – that's great fun! | *Pretend to hold a piece of cake nearer and nearer mouth until finally it's eaten.* |

Ann Bryant

# I mustn't go to sleep

It's 11 o'clock,
I'm waiting for Santa.
Everyone was in bed an hour ago,
And I mustn't go to sleep.

Mince pies still intact,
He's bringing me a computer,
A Gameboy and a bike.
And I mustn't go to sleep.

Wine still untouched,
Decorations sparkling.
And I mustn't go to... sleep,
And I mustn't... go... to....

Adam Nuckley, aged 12

# It's Christmas Eve

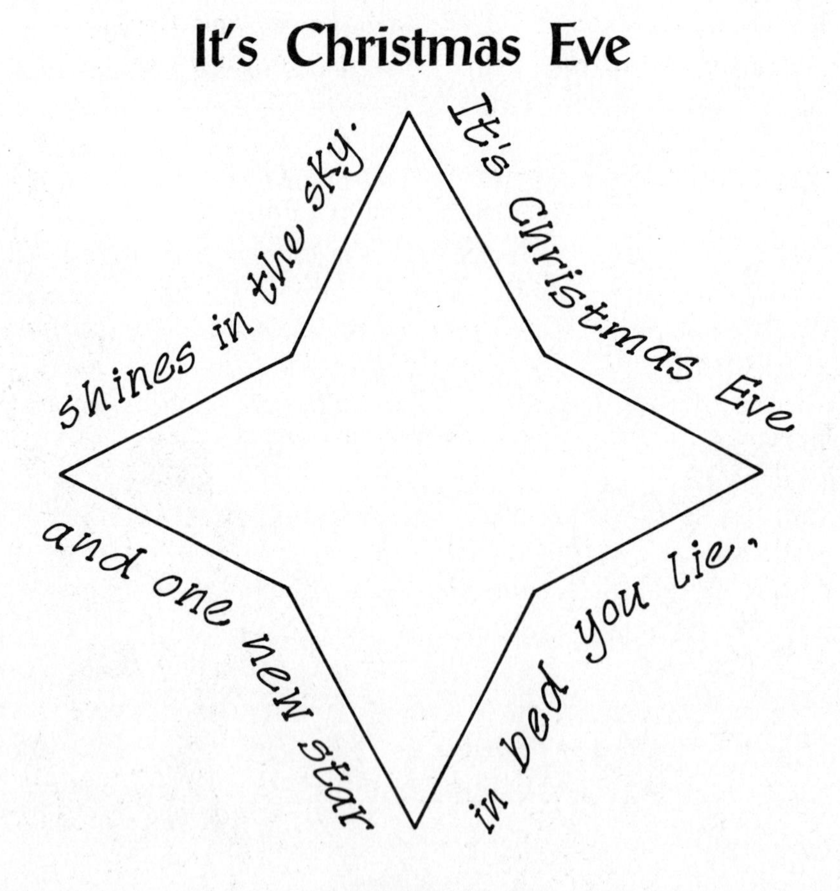


Wes Magee

# Christmas Eve

...is a journey on a turbulent tube train,
lots of ecstatic stations, really packed
and you're grabbing on
to whatever you can get hold of.

There's Mrs Lang and Matthew and Natasha
visiting grandparents for Christmas.

There's silent business people
travelling to their office blocks
for parties.
Afterwards they'll come back
shouting, staggering, singing, full of wine.

There's Ben and Ezra and Sophie and Becky
and Craig and Seema and Joshua and Kelly
travelling to see their mates.

Christmas Eve is black
with red bubbles of excitement.

It's a match when we're losing 2–0
five minutes from the end
and we win 3–2.

Daniel Sedgwick, aged 10

# Christmas night

The cold wind echoes under the door and chills the hearts
Of those that Christmas has not reached.
They strain their ears hopefully
For that merry knock on the door of carol singers
Or the cheery crackle of the fire as it burns contentedly.
Instead they hear the snow gently falling
And forming a blanket of silence over the land.
They sit locked in darkness, dreaming of presents brightly wrapped,
A freshly cut Christmas tree adorned with coloured lights,
The gently wafting smell of turkey fresh from the oven,
The merry note of carols dancing around the tree:
This is the Christmas they will never know or see.

Amy Iversen, aged 14

# Questions on Christmas Eve

But *how* can his reindeer fly without wings?
Jets on their hooves? That's plain cheating!
And *how* can he climb down the chimney pot
when we've got central heating?

You say it's all magic and I shouldn't ask
about Santa on Christmas Eve.
But I'm confused by the stories I've heard:
I don't know what to believe.

I said that I'd sit up in bed all night long
to see if he really would call.
But I fell fast asleep, woke up after dawn
as something banged in the hall.

I saw my sock crammed with apples and sweets;
there were parcels piled high near the door.
Jingle bells tinkled far off in the dark.
One snowflake shone on the floor.

Wes Magee

# Santa Claus is Superman!

I was lying in bed the other night
When suddenly, I saw the light!
It's clear as day, I must be right –
Santa Claus is Superman!

I've been cunning, used my wits,
I've pieced together all the bits.
And glory be! The whole thing fits:
Santa Claus is Superman!

Where's Clark Kent on Christmas Eve?
In Smallville, he'd have you believe.
What do you think I am? Naive?
Santa Claus is Superman!

And where's Father Christmas the rest of the year?
Funny how he just seems to – disappear.
He's in Metropolis – it's clear!
Santa Claus is Superman!

You might say it's a pack of lies –
One's dark, one's fair – they're a different size.
Haven't you heard the word 'disguise'?
Santa Claus is Superman!

Tell me who else has the speed,
I mean, the kind of speed you'd need?
It's obvious, are we agreed?
Santa Claus is Superman!

And who else is there strong enough.
To carry all that Christmas stuff?
Admit it now, I now it's tough,
Santa Claus *is* Superman!

Colin McNaughton

# Santa Claus and Company

In the still and frosty night
Stand the reindeer, poised for flight;
Their breath is seen on frosty air,
Their feet are restless, waiting there.

The sleigh is packed and riding low
In drifts of newly fallen snow;
Its bursting sides filled to the top
With toys to leave at every stop.

When Santa sashes through the door
With heavy pace, more gifts in store,
The reindeer strain, their stances taut,
The starlight in their harness caught.

With waves and shouts and gleeful 'Hey'
Old Santa jumps into the sleigh;
And off they fly with breathless pace
To worlds below in boundless space.

Flying, flying, flying, climbing, climbing, climbing,
Sailing, sailing, sailing, drifting, drifting, drifting,
Over, under, through and around
All the clouds, their path is wound.

This night their task is one of joy,
To bring to every girl and boy
Something wished for all the year
And now, in Santa's sleigh, so near.

Anticipation, palpitation, exhilaration, expectation!
All the 'ations' in creation
Can't describe the great elation
Of Santa Claus and Company.

LaVonne Guenther

# Dear Santa...

Dear Santa, when its Christmas,
and you finally appear
after all those weeks of waiting,
please don't give presents this year

to Daddy because he tells me off
for swinging on my chair,
to Mummy because it really hurts
when she runs a comb through my hair.

To my big brother Benjamin
who's awfully mean to me,
and to little sister Sara
who's on at me constantly.

To cousins Jill and Josephine
who are dreadful little pests,
and to my teacher at school
who sets such difficult tests.

To the rabbit who tries to bite me
and the crazy cat next door,
to the dog who lays in my way
so I trip and fall on the floor.

To the man across the road
who never smiles or waves,
and to my grumpy neighbour
who tells me to behave.

And please don't listen if they should say
that I deserve nothing too.
I know you won't believe them,
I've put my faith in you.

I'm always good and kind,
I'm careful and I'm clever,
and I'm never nasty to anyone,
not ever...!

Brian Moses

# Christmas past

We didn't go in for Christmas trees
in our house, too messy, I suppose;
just gnome-high artificial jobs, one
in the hall, one on the dining room table.

I don't remember having fairy lights,
electrical circuits were never my father's
scene. But we did have tree decorations,
shining balls, tinsel, golden stars on top,

and one glass Father Christmas. We unwrapped
him from dusty tissue every year, replaced
the broken loop with cotton, put him in place.
Our childhood passed his black-smudged gaze.

And still he hangs on, living through spring
and summer in the dark places of the loft.
I cherish his lack-lustre body, treat him
with respect and make the children laugh.

'Get a new one, mum,' they say. 'This old
guy's long past his best!' Our tree, forest-
felled, blazes with light. And still,
broken-backed, the ghost-bauble smiles on.

Moira Andrew

# Tom's up the tree

Our kitten has climbed up the Christmas tree.
He looks so funny there.
His tail is swishing madly
His eyes are wide and stare.

He's tangled up in the tinsel,
He's knocked off a silver bell.
His fur is spiky with needles
And he's chewed up a cracker as well.

Mum says he's very naughty
And I'm afraid he will fall.
But Dad just laughs and says that Tom
Is the best decoration of all.

Eileen Gladston

# Crackers

| | |
|---|---|
| Sit down for your tea. | *All children should sit down in a circle.* |
| Put your hands on your knee. | *Put hands on knees.* |
| Pull the cracker 1, 2, 3. | *Turn to partners, hold hands and pull.* |
| And out jumps...[insert a child's name each time]. | *The child whose name is called should jump up.* |

Ann Bryant

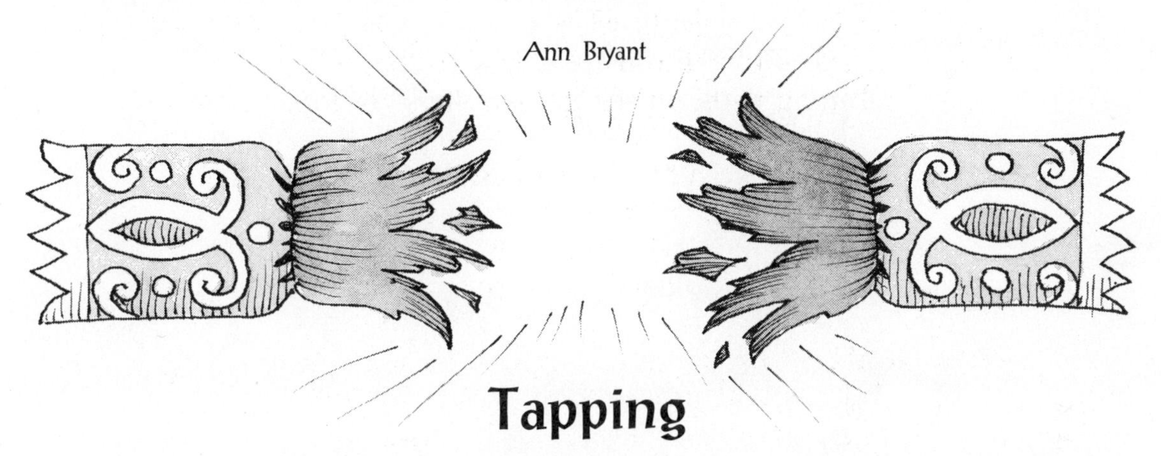

# Tapping

*The children can do the actions for this poem and then make up their own ideas of what could be in the parcel!*

| | |
|---|---|
| Tapping on my present<br>Whatever could it be? | *Tap imaginary present.* |
| Rattling my present<br>Whatever could it be? | *Rattle imaginary present.* |
| Snipping the ribbons<br>Whatever could it be? | *Snip imaginary ribbons.* |
| Opening it up<br>And what do we see? | *Open imaginary box.* |
| The bounciest ball<br>To bounce in the air | *Pretend to bounce a ball.* |
| A long woolly scarf<br>For me to wear | *Wrap scarf round neck.* |
| Rings for my fingers | *Wiggle fingers.* |
| Brushes for my hair | *Brush hair.* |
| Sweeties for me<br>And my brother to share. | *Deal out sweets, 'one for me, one for you,' style.* |
| A big bright book | *Open out praying hands.* |
| And a cuddly brown bear | *Pretend to cuddle a bear.* |
| A toffee apple | *Pretend to hold up stick in one hand.* |
| And a marzipan pear | *Hold up stick in other hand.* |
| Open it up and what do we see? | *Pretend to open parcel.* |
| My own blue camera just for me. | *Pretend to take a photograph.* |

Ann Bryant

# Bundles

A bundle is a funny thing,
It always sets me wondering:
For whether it is thick or wide
You never know just what's inside.

Especially in Christmas week
Temptation is too great to peek!
Now wouldn't it be much more fun
If shoppers carried things undone?

John Farrar

# The present

I got a drum for Christmas.
I beat it night and day,
'Cause if I didn't practise,
I'd never learn to play.

I **bang** it in the bathtub,
I **thump** it in the den,
And even when I'm sleeping
I **whack** it now and then.

My mummy's wearing ear-plugs,
My daddy's door is closed,
And Uncle Jim, whose gift it was,
Has got a bloody nose.

Mary Blakeslee

# What did you have for Christmas?

I woke on Christmas morning
feeling woolly in my head –
had Santa Claus forgotten
to leave presents by my bed?

But there I was – covered all over
in lots and lots
of very itchy bright red spots
sprinkled around
like polka dots!

I tried on my new nurses' set,
flipped through each picture book –
but I wasn't one bit interested.
I called, 'Mum, come and look!'

And there I was – covered all over
in lots and lots
of very itchy bright red spots
sprinkled around
like polka dots!

Mum said, 'It's measles, my girl.
Back to bed and snuggle down.'
I saw myself in the glass in the hall,
I looked like a circus clown.

For there I was – covered all over
in lots and lots
of very itchy bright red spots
sprinkled around
like polka dots!

They trundled me into the living room
so I'd see everything from my bed
the tree, the lights, the Christmas crib –
but I slept, a party hat on my head.

So there I was – covered all over
in lots and lots
of very itchy bright red spots
sprinkled around
like polka dots!

And that's what I had for Christmas!

Moira Andrew

# Our family's taking back Christmas shopping list!

a winter coat – too big, too colourful, too expensive,

a pocket game – wouldn't work, wouldn't fit in my pocket,

a digital watch – dead battery, dead beat,

a radio controlled car – went out of control, went out of the window,

a moving doll – turned it on – head fell off – turned it off,

a pair of shorts – the elastic snapped, the trousers fell down,

a hair dryer – won't go, won't blow,

a pair of tights – kept snagging, kept sagging,

a new perfume – wrong sort, wrong pong,

a plastic football – one hard kick, one flat ball,

a mountain bike – brakes slammed on, brakes jammed on,

a pair of socks – too small, two left feet.

And if Santa had been around we would have taken him back
or on second thoughts perhaps we would have given him the sack!

Ian Souter

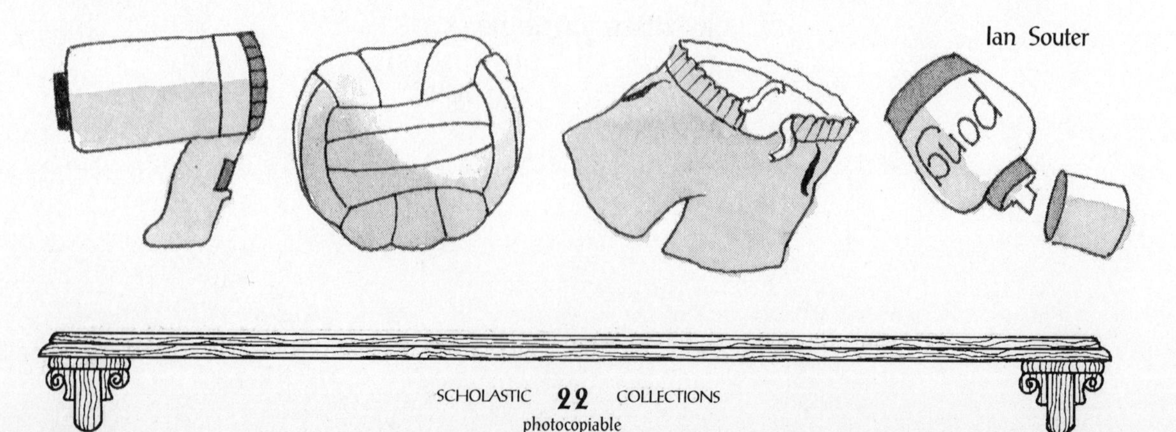

## Christmas morn

Chiming bells ring out clear
The echo now you can hear.
Soft snow falls from above
falls on the landscape as white as a dove.

Pure white snow outside,
Silver tinsel glitters.
Presents hanging on a tree,
The glowing firelight flickers.

The golden sun in the morning
Lights the snowy landscape,
Ice is melting slowly
on the frozen lake.

Benedict Taylor, aged 10

## Christmas is here

Stars aflickering beautifully up high.
Outside snow is falling.
In the morning
children yawning.
Open presents quickly.
I creep downstairs,
Take a peep at all the treats.
Christmas is here.

Rebecca Byrne, aged 10

# Christmas Day

It was waking early and making a din.
It was knowing that for the next twenty minutes
 I'd never be quite so excited again.
It was singing the last verse of
 'O Come all Ye Faithful', the one that's
 only meant to be sung on Christmas Day.
It was lighting a fire in the unused room
 and a draught that blew back woodsmoke
 into our faces.
It was lunch and a full table,
 and dad repeating how he'd once eaten his
 off the bonnet of a lorry in Austria.
It was keeping quiet for the Queen
 and Gran telling that one about children
 being seen but not heard.
 (As if we could get a word in edgeways
 once she started!)
It was 'Monopoly' and me out to cheat the Devil
 to be the first to reach Mayfair.
It was, 'Just a small one for the lad,'
 and dad saying, 'We don't want him getting tiddly.'
It was aunts assaulting the black piano
 and me keeping clear of mistletoe
 in case they trapped me.
It was pinning a tail on the donkey,
 and nuts that wouldn't crack
 and crackers that pulled apart but didn't bang.

And then when the day was almost gone,
 it was Dad on the stairs,
 on his way to bed,
 and one of us saying:
 'You've forgotten to take your hat off....'
 And the purple or pink or orange paper
 still crowning his head.

Brian Moses

# Our family Christmas

Christmas for my mum is...

staggering with Christmas shopping,
wrestling with Christmas presents
and sweltering over Christmas cooking
until she begins to resemble the Christmas turkey.
Red, hot and bothered.

Christmas for my dad is...

struggling with the Christmas tree,
muddling with the Christmas lights
and falling off the ladder twice
until eventually he can be found
resting his eyes on the sofa.
We don't know which to plug in
dad or the lights!

Christmas for my sister is...

excitement crackling in her eyes
as she waits for presents to arrive.
Helping dad with the decorations,
some of which are made of chocolate.
Every time he turns round
somehow another one just disappears!

Christmas for our dog is...

simple!
She can't believe her luck.
THERE'S A TREE IN THE FRONT ROOM!
And the odd pink bauble hanging from it
which she loves to crunch.

Christmas for our family is...

Christmas Day finally arriving
along with grandma and grandad.
One great big parcel of
excitement, fun and warmth
which we all in our own way enjoy unwrapping.

Ian Souter

# A gift from the stars

On Christmas Eve, on the first chime of midnight
the Christmas King and the Queen of Christmas
take the new moon, sharp as a blade,
and slit the thin paper sky.

They help each other wrap up the frosty stars
in the night's dark blue wrapping paper;
the Queen stretches out her sparkling hand
and grasps a passing comet to use as a gift tag.

The Queen of Christmas and the Christmas King
then take their present on a long journey:
they slide past the icy meteorites,
they glide between the glassy suns,
they slink in and out of cosmic clouds,
they skim the outer edges of planets' rings,
making their way through the caves and caverns of space
to this shining Earth, to this cold country,
to this snowy town, to this still street,
to this sleeping house, to this quiet bedroom,
to this soft bed
and place their sky gift on your pillow.

And ping!
the second you open your eyes on Christmas morn
the parcel bursts open without a sound
and showers you with frosty stars
that zing and spin and melt and split and vanish
to become miniscule molecules of
Happy Christmasness.

John Rice

# The colours of Christmas

Christmas is white.
An innocent carpet, frosted like sugar on a cake,
Delicate white crystals sparkle in watery sunrays.
The angelic glow from a tree-top fairy,
The sauce trickles down hot, spicy pudding.
And mistletoe hangs in expectation.

Christmas is red.
The scarlet robust chest of the robin,
Bloodshot berry clusters, succulent and polished,
Smart red ribbons furnish front doors.
Ice chilled noses, frost kissed cheeks,
And Santa's curiosity bag.

Christmas is green.
Dishes laden with wrapped delights,
Party dresses sway and rustle.
A festive redolence of pine from a decorated tree.
Prickly holly intertwined with ivy.
And faces green with envy.

Sarah Copeland, aged 13

# It's Christmas!

**C**arols drift across the night
**H**olly gleams by candlelight
**R**oaring fire; a spooky tale
**I**ce and snow and wind and hail
**S**anta seen in a High Street store
**T**elevision... more and *more*
**M**ince pies, turkey, glass of wine
**A**cting your own pantomime
**S**ocks hung up. It's Christmas time!

Wes Magee

# Christmas

Holly and mistletoe,
Fat robins on cards,
Sparkling shop windows,
Large winking stars.

Bright lights in the high street,
Carols in the square,
Arms full of parcels,
Frost in the air.

Parties and pantomime,
Nativity plays,
Christmas is a special time,
In so many ways.

Eileen Gladston

# Christmas poem

Dazzling presents wrapped,
under the tree.
Shining tinsel as you can see,
Freezing ice gleams,
In children's dreams,
And now it is Christmas for you and me.

Rudolph is flying,
And Santa is spying
On children who are bad and good,
Turkey is roasting and pheasant too,
Bells in the churchyard are chiming for you.

Robert Brown and Greg Shepherd, aged 10

# Once there was a cold country

Once there was a cold country
and in that cold country
was a cold county
and in that cold county
was a cold town
and in that cold town
was a cold road
and in that cold road
was a nice warm house
and in that nice warm house
was a young boy
with his mum
putting up the Christmas tree.
But out in the snowy garden
was poor dad
hanging out the washing.

David Minks, aged 8

# A week to Christmas

Sunday with six whole days to go.
How we'll endure it I don't know!

Monday the goodies are in the making,
Spice smells of pudding and mince pies a-baking.

Tuesday, Dad's home late and quiet as a mouse
He smuggles packages into the house.

Wednesday's the day for decorating the tree,
Will the lights work again? We'll have to see.

Thursday's for last minute shopping and hurry,
We've never seen Mum in quite such a flurry!

Friday is Christmas Eve when we lie awake
Trying to sleep before the day break

And that special quiet on Christmas morn
When out there somewhere Christ was born.

John Cotton

# Christmas riddles

My slender figure charms,
Dressed in white or bright colours.
The frills of my dress grow and gather
As I grow smaller,
Lighting your celebratory tree.
A comfort in the darkness,
A small welcoming warmth.

A steaming richness,
A fruity companion,
A cannon ball for not firing
Though I sometimes flame.
I complete your feast
With my green buttonhole
And yellow waistcoat.

Watery bones,
Transparent pencils,
Cold fingers pointing out from the eaves,
A fringe of lances.

Brightly dressed mysteries,
Joyous surprises and exciters of hopes,
Tokens of love,
Affection's messengers,
Containing annual delights.

Sent from the corners of the round world,
A blue uniformed messenger delivers them.
Small pictures of friendship,
Making a mantelshelf gallery of goodwill.

---

I am busy when you are abed.
I feel strange in my disguise
Like an oversize robin
That has been out in the snow.
I creep stealthily to avoid detection
Although I know I am welcome.

---

Rain polishes
My round the year gloss,
Honing my row
Of sharp spears.
In winter I come into my own,
Bearing the crown
And gifts
Of bright beads of blood.

John Cotton

*(Answers: Candle, Christmas pudding, Icicles, Presents, Christmas cards, Father Christmas, Holly)*

# Christmas haikus

**Candle**

That feather of flame
melting the window's ice skin
guides us through the night.

**Holly sprig**

Berries like blood drops
and green leaves to remind us
spring sleeps beyond the hill.

**Christmas bells**

Urgent, they call us
across fields to a barn where
cows, a donkey stand.

**Robin**

As heavy snow falls
he's a red-vested Batman
on the garden fence.

Wes Magee

# Scarecrow Christmas

In winter fields
a scarecrow sings
the hopeful tune
of lonely kings.

His empty heart
is thin and cold,
his cruel rags
are worn and old.

But in our homes
we sing out clear,
warm words of joy
and know no fear.

In bed at night
we listen for,
padded footsteps
at the door.

In other fields
and different lands,
living scarecrows
reach out hands.

They live beneath
the sun's cruel rays.
They do not know
of Christmas days.

Pie Corbett

# In a dark wood

In a dark wood
there was a large fir tree
and in that large fir tree
was a small branch
and on that small branch
there was a little nest
and in the little nest
there were some tiny robins
and suddenly
an insignificant snowflake
landed there.

Brrrr.

Rosemary Crabb Wyke, aged 9

# The snowman

We have built a big snowman,
We all think he is great.
And we have built him at the end of our street.
He has a big, round body
And a small, round head
But he hasn't any feet.

We gave him coal for his eyes,
A carrot for his nose,
In his mouth we have put an old pipe.
He has a hat on his head
And a scarf round his neck
And that makes him look just right.

When we look out of the window
And we see him standing there,
Oh, how we all wish that he would stay.
But when the weather changes
And the sun comes out,
He will simply melt away.

Eileen Gladston

# Snowman

| | |
|---|---|
| I build the snowman, build the snowman | *Place one hand on top of other, keeping palms flat, building upwards.* |
| Build the snowman tall. | |
| I put the snowman's hat on, | *Put hands on head.* |
| It's a great big ball. | *Show a ball shape.* |
| A carrot for his nose | *Pretend to draw out your nose.* |
| Coal for his eyes | *Pretend to look through binoculars.* |
| And buttons down his tummy | *Prod from neck down to tummy* |
| For a big surprise! | *ending with a big prod on tummy!* |
| Hey Mr Snowman, I want you to stay! | *Wag finger as if telling someone off.* |
| But the sun's come out | *Fingers of both hands splayed.* |
| And he's melting away. | *Gentle descending fingers.* |

Ann Bryant

# With icicles hanging

| | |
|---|---|
| With icicles hanging in nice, little rows, | *Dangle fingers down like icicles.* |
| You'd best button buttons and cover your nose! | *Cover nose with hand.* |
| DO wear your mittens and hat, if you please, | *Pat head.* |
| And hurry inside if you happen to sneeze! | *Ah choo!* |

Anonymous

## Winter song

'I've been here too long'
Says the Man in the Moon,
Floating over the tops
Of the hazels in Hazel Copse.
'I've sung my song.'

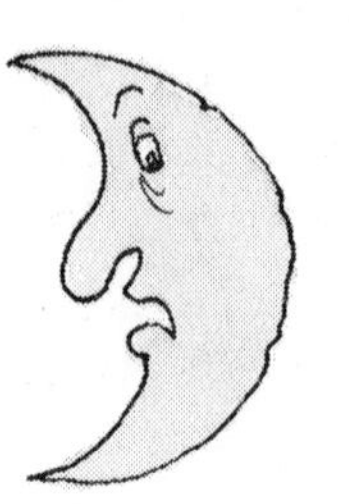

'Same goes for me too'
Says Jack Frost, crisply.
'Want to be on my own
For a good think and moan.
My sparkling is through.'

It's all gone too far.
Santa's waited and sweated
In his last grotto
With his last doll and lotto,
Transformer and car.

And Winter and Frost
And the Moon turn in
On themselves. Girls and boys
Search out a new noise
For the ones lost.

'What's that?' say the lakes
As the new words swirl
Over stone ground
Like leaves.
'It's the sound
The children's song makes.'

Fred Sedgwick

## The school field in December

Hundreds of
Wellington boots
have trampled the snow
until the field
glitters like a rink.

Snowmen stand
rigid with cold.
Squeals of children
skate across this acre
of Arctic ice.

Wes Magee

# STORIES

## Mrs Christmas and the sleeping polar bear

At last the magic hour had arrived! It was time for Father Christmas to leave on his annual Christmas Eve trip. Mrs Christmas checked to see whether Father Christmas and his three most trustworthy elves, Farnsworth, Groff and Callahan, were all snugly buttoned up.

'Now be sure to wear your scarves,' she reminded them in her brisk, matter-of-fact manner. 'Flying about in an open sleigh isn't the warmest way to travel.'

'Yes dear,' Father Christmas replied, hastily. He kissed Mrs Christmas goodbye. Then he and his elves headed for the sleigh barn carrying their Christmas sacks. Callahan reached the sleigh first. What he saw made him drop his sacks in astonishment. He scampered excitedly back to the others.

'You'll never believe what's in the sleigh!' he squealed.

'What?' cried Father Christmas.

'A polar bear!' said Callahan.

They all rushed over to the sleigh. There on the back seat lay an enormous white polar bear. Snoring.

'It's a polar bear, all right!' gasped Groff. 'A great sleeping polar bear!'

'Polar bears usually dig caves in the snow and use them for dens,' said Farnsworth. 'Why is this polar bear sleeping in our sleigh?'

'We haven't got time to wonder why he's here,' said Father Christmas. 'We must worry about how we're going to get this huge sleeping bear out of the sleigh.'

'Maybe we could take him with us,' suggested Callahan.

'No room,' Father Christmas replied.

'We'll have to wake him up then,' said Groff. 'Very gently of course.'

Father Christmas and the elves began poking the bear gently in his ribs. He did not stir. They poked him harder. They shook him. They yanked at his thick hairy coat. They whistled in his ears. He did not wake up. He just went on snoring.

'I have an idea,' said Callahan. 'Let's pull him out of the sleigh.'

It was getting later and later. Quickly they tied a strong rope around the polar bear's middle. They pulled and pulled, tugged and tugged. They huffed and puffed, groaned and moaned. But the big white bear didn't budge an inch. He simply went on snoring.

'Oh, dear!' said Father Christmas. 'Time's flying, but we're not. What do we do now?'

'I suggest we tip the bear out,' said Farnsworth. 'If we all push hard enough maybe we can upset the sleigh.'

Father Christmas and the elves lined up on the right-hand side of the sleigh. They pushed and pushed. They shoved and shoved. They thumped and bumped. But the sleigh did not turn over. Neither did the polar bear. He simply went on snoring.

'Oh dear!' puffed Father Christmas. 'We should have taken off half an hour ago. And that bear is going to sleep 'til spring!'

Just then Mrs Christmas came hurrying into the barn. 'Haven't you gone yet?' she scolded. 'The children are waiting! What's the hold up?'

Callahan pointed to the sleigh. 'A sleeping polar bear. We just can't wake him up or get him off the back seat.'

Mrs Christmas stood thinking. She tapped her foot, rubbed her nose and blinked. Suddenly, she reached down into one of the Christmas sacks and brought out an armful of candy canes. She began waving one cane under the bear's nose.

Suddenly the polar bear opened one eye, then the other eye. He sat up, stretched and looked longingly at the candy cane. His mouth began to water.

Sleepily the bear crawled down from the back seat. He lumbered toward Mrs Christmas. She gave him a candy cane. When that was gone she gave him another, then another and another. And each time she walked backward a few steps. She fed the polar bear candy canes until they reached the tall snow bank by the side of the barn.

'There,' she said, 'dig yourself a nice warm cave and rest yourself for as long as you want.'

'How did you know candy canes would waken the polar bear, my dear?' asked Father Christmas.

'Why, anyone with a grain of common sense knows that bears can't resist honey and sweets,' Mrs Christmas replied. 'The very smell of sweets will waken even the sleepiest bear. Now, do hitch up the reindeer, and fly along. And don't forget your scarves.' With that, Mrs Christmas bustled back to the house.

In no time at all Father Christmas and his elves were off and away, skimming the snowy tree-tops, glistening in the light of the moon. 'That wife of mine has a lot of common sense, I must admit,' chuckled Father Christmas. 'But I never dreamed she knew how to waken a sleeping polar bear!'

Frances B. Watts

# Bedding down for winter

Mouse pushed her little nose up from under the pile of leaves and wriggled her way out into the daylight. She sniffed the air.

It was nearly the middle of winter, and only a week to go until her babies were due on Christmas Eve. Her heart gave a pit-a-pat of excitement at the thought – but her joy was tinged with fear at the prospect of even colder weather to come.

She had plenty of food arranged neatly in little rows in the special storehouse that she had stocked so carefully during the summer – an abundance of acorns, a hoard of hazelnuts that she'd come across quite by accident one fine morning on her way to get a drink, and a choice collection of chestnuts that she'd found in the corner of the field where the children used to play. She had apples from the orchard, wheat and oats from the cornfield and a good supply of water in upturned acorn-cups. No – she was all right for food.

It was the cold she was worried about. Last winter two of her neighbour's children had died in the severe frost that had penetrated deep into the earth making even the best-lined nests chilly little places.

She thought long and hard. If only she could find some sort of special protection that would keep the cold out and the warmth in....

Out on the lake the ducks swam lazily. It was odd, mused Mouse, that they didn't seem to feel the cold. Why, she had seen them once trying to land on a frozen lake, and right fools they had made of themselves – sliding and skating and skidding on to their tails, squawking with rage and embarrassment. She smiled at the thought, remembering how ungainly they'd looked as they tried to take off again with their webbed feet flapping and cracking against the hard surface.

However, the lake was not yet frozen and they were happy enough there today. Mouse felt hungry and made her way down to the farmyard, past the lake, through the hedge, across the ditch, along the lane and into the barn where the ducks slept at night. She began to rummage around.

What a jumble of things there were! Bits of hay, old scraps of blankets, pieces of newspaper, fragments of clothing, feathers from the hens and lots of little balls of downy fluff from the soft necks of the ducks. My, they looked warm....

Mouse sat back, cleaned her whiskers and thought. What a marvellous lining they would make for the babies' nursery – but how on earth could she get them back? 'I can't take mouthfuls of it,' she thought. 'I'd choke! No, what I need is something to carry it in.'

Out she scurried into the farmyard, her nose twitching and her mind racing. She'd have to get some sort of container, but it would have to be small. After all, she was only a *little* mouse. And it would have to be strong so as not to fall to pieces when she carried it... a sort of pouch, she decided.

Mouse heard the latch of the farmhouse door rattle. It was Farmer's Wife opening the door. Mouse hid. She didn't want the contents of the teapot thrown all over her. Farmer's Wife came out every day and emptied the pot of used tea-bags on to the bases of the roses that climbed up on either side of the porch. It was a tip she'd heard on the radio. Today was no exception. Sploosh! And a pile of fresh tea-bags settled alongside the old ones.

Mouse stared at the tea-bags, and slowly, very slowly an idea began to form in her head. The more she thought of it, the better it became. Swiftly, she sped over to the roses and pulled out a dried tea-bag. She gnawed neatly along one side and tipped out all the leaves, shaking it till it was empty. Then, with the bag clasped firmly between her teeth, she made her way in a series of hops and runs, round the walls of the farmyard and into the barn.

Working at fever-pitch, she stuffed as many little balls of duck down as she could into the empty tea-bag. Once it was full she set out on the long journey home. Away out of the barn, along the lane, across the ditch, through the hedge, past the lake to the pile of leaves, and under the leaves to her home.

Her little heart beat with excitement as she scrambled into the nest. She tugged the tea-bag into the bedroom.

Oh, how beautiful it was! Soft, warm and springy – and there was plenty more where that come from! Back and forth she beavered until all the dried tea-bags were full of the lovely down. Then she spread out the still-wet bags and left them to dry in the sun under the roses. Exhausted, she trudged home to sleep.

By the end of the week the whole of the floor of the nest and halfway up the walls was covered and lined with soft downy tea-bags.

Mouse's eyes shone with happiness. Now she could *really* look forward to Christmas and her new babies!

Back at the farmhouse Farmer's Wife was busy wrapping the down-filled quilts she had bought her daughters for Christmas. She knew the girls would be thrilled with their new bedding!

Christmas Day dawned. In the farmhouse the children shouted with delight at their presents. 'How lovely!' they exclaimed as they flung the quilts on their beds and snuggled up warmly under them. And in a cosy nest, along the lane, across the ditch, through the hedge, past the lake and under the leaves, six new pink baby mice also lay snug and warm in their eiderdown home.

C. Walsh

# From favours to crackers

Once a year, in December, there was a 'topsy-turvy' festival in Ancient Rome. It was called Saturnalia, because it was in honour of the Roman god Saturn. At this festival, owners and slaves changed places for a day. Slaves gave orders, and owners obeyed them.

In the middle of the Saturnalia festival, there was a feast. Everyone, owners and slaves alike, sat down together to enjoy it. (No one knows who did the cooking – or the washing up.) At the feast, people gave each other 'favours'. These were small presents of nuts, sweets, coins, tiny statues of animals, birds and Saturn, god of the festival. The 'favours' were intended to bring good luck; the word 'favour' comes from a Latin word meaning 'helps'.

Ancient Chinese people gave each other favours too. But they were a different kind. They were messages of good luck, written on pieces of rice paper and baked into cakes and biscuits. Before you ate, you broke open the cake or biscuit to find the paper and read the message. Some people went on to eat it (rice paper is easy to digest). In that way, they thought that they took the good luck inside themselves.

The idea of favours has lasted. At feasts and parties today, people often put small presents, called 'charms' beside each place at the table. They are things like tiny models of animals, people, flowers, cars or bells. In many countries, you can still buy Chinese 'fortune cookies'.

Sometimes, in those places where Christmas is celebrated, people give each other favours, usually at dinner-time or tea-time on Christmas Day. These favours come in crackers. A man called Tom Smith, a sweet maker, invented crackers over 150 years ago.

Nowadays, sweets are usually made in factories, on production lines. But in Tom Smith's time, they were hand-made, in kitchens at the back of the sweet shop. They were sold loose, in paper packets rather like ice-cream cones. You decided how many you wanted – one or two, or as many as half a pound. The shop assistant then took a piece of paper, twisted it into a cone of exactly the right size, and put in your sweets with a small, long-handled shovel or a pair of tongs.

Most modern sweet companies make the same kinds of sweets: chocolates, mints, fruit gums, boiled sweets, licorice allsorts. But in Tom Smith's time, each shopkeeper tried to make his or her own sweets special, unlike anyone else's. Tom Smith used to say, 'People like novelty. If you want to sell, make something *new*!' He not only invented new kinds of sweets, but packaged them in different ways, with pretty paper, ribbons and bows.

In 1846 Tom Smith and his wife went to France for a holiday. At least, it was a holiday for Mrs Smith. Tom Smith wasn't interested in walking by the river, seeing the sights, enjoying the parks and gardens. All he wanted to do was look in sweet-shop windows, and see how French shopkeepers sold their sweets. He was particularly pleased to see how they dealt with sugared almonds. Instead of shovelling them into cones, they wrapped each sweet separately, in a twist of coloured paper.

As soon as the Smiths got home, Tom also began wrapping his sweets individually. People flocked to his shop to buy. Then someone said, 'What surprise have you in store for next year, Mr Smith?' Tom thought hard. Then he remembered favours, the good-luck charms and mottoes people had given at parties for over two thousand years.

That Christmas, when people untwisted their wrapped sweets bought at Smith's, they found a second layer of paper inside the wrapping. On it was a motto, such as 'Sweets for a sweetheart' or 'For the one I love'. This was a delicious idea: you could eat your sweet, think about your sweetheart – and no one but you would know.

The next year, Tom Smith's twists held even more. In each was a sweet, a motto *and* a good-luck charm. But they were not too successful – and he couldn't work out why. He was sitting by the fire, thinking the problem over, when the yule-log suddenly crackled and sparked in the flames. 'Got it!' he thought. 'I'll make my twists into crackers too!'

This was harder than he'd imagined. The cracks had to be safe – no huge explosions, no fires, no burned fingers or smarting eyes. At last Tom worked out a way. He made two strips of card for each cracker. The end of each strip was dipped in chemicals, and the strips were stuck lightly together. When two people pulled them apart, the chemicals rubbed together to make a tiny fizz and bang. This was the 'crack' that made the cracker.

That Christmas, crackers were a sensation. As well as the 'crack', each held a sweet, a paper hat, a motto and a novelty: a mask, puzzle, game or toy – just like the 'favours' of olden days. All were contained in a cardboard tube in a twist of coloured paper. Tom Smith's fortune was made. In the months that followed, he opened a factory, and was soon exporting Christmas crackers all round the world.

Since Tom Smith's time, crackers have been made of all shapes and sizes. Russian princes and princesses, a hundred years ago, used to give each other crackers filled not with favours, but with rings, necklaces, perfume, even flowers and tiny fans made of gold and jewels. The biggest cracker ever known was made for a stage show, a Christmas pantomime. It was two metres long, and when the actors pulled it there was a huge flash of coloured light, and all kinds of glittering stage costumes tumbled out, as well as hundreds of ordinary-sized crackers to give the audience.

What do you expect from a Christmas cracker nowadays? A fancy hat? A motto? A riddle? A favour? Mass-produced crackers can be fun. But why not make your own, specially filled for each member of the family? You can buy 'cracks' and party hats in a novelty shop. Then all you need is some cardboard for tubes, some pretty paper, a small present suitable for each person, and good luck-mottoes, jokes and messages all your own. It's easy!

Kenneth McLeish

# Alfred's shoes

Alfred sat on his little blue chair. A huge tear rolled down his cheek, fell off his chin and landed on the shoes in his lap. It was these shoes that made him so unhappy. Alfred's shoes did not pinch his toes, or rub blisters on his heels, or hurt his ankles. The trouble with Alfred's shoes was that the tips wouldn't stay curled up.

Alfred was an elf who worked for Father Christmas. For an elf who worked for Father Christmas to be unhappy was most unusual. But for an elf who worked for Father Christmas to have straight shoes was even more unusual.

When Alfred first came to work for Father Christmas, his shoes were just like any other elf's and he was very happy. He was excited about making toys for girls and boys around the world. The great workroom was filled with the noise of tapping hammers, and the elves laughed and sang as they worked together. Alfred could hardly wait to begin. His first assignment was in the musical toys department.

'Work carefully,' said the Chief Inspector. 'Watch the older elves and you will learn to make perfect musical toys.'

'I will, I will,' Alfred solemnly promised.

For an hour he watched carefully and worked slowly. It was taking him a long time to finish one drum. Alfred was eager to make a horn. A set of bells. And some cymbals. So he began to hurry.

A few hours later the Chief Inspector came to check on him. The Chief Inspector thumped the drum. It made a flat sound. He blew the horn. It squeaked. He rang the bells. Their ding was too soft. He clashed the cymbals. They cracked.

The Chief Inspector shook his head. 'This will never do,' he said. 'Maybe we had better try you in another department.' At this moment

Alfred's shoes began to uncurl a little, but not enough to be noticed.

Alfred was transferred to the moving toys department where he worked carefully for a while. His tiny cars and trucks rolled merrily across the floor. His trains tooted as they went round and round on the track. His aeroplanes looked as if they were ready to take off at a moment's notice. Then one day Alfred made a boat too quickly, and it sank to the bottom of the test tank with an enormous 'glub!'

The Chief Inspector clicked his tongue. The toes of Alfred's shoes uncurled a little more.

Soon Alfred was transferred to the doll department. He did not stay there very long, however, because dolls require extra careful work and Alfred was too impatient. The toes of his shoes uncurled a little more.

Finally, he was sent to the stuffed animal department. Everyone hoped Alfred would do well there. They said 'Don't hurry, Alfred. Work carefully. Watch us.'

It was about this time that the toes of Alfred's shoes really began to bother him. At first he was bothered because they did not look right, but now they were getting so straight that they got in his way. He had trouble climbing up and down stairs. And when work was over and the elves ran outside to play, Alfred would stumble over his toes.

The other elves started to tease him. They always made him 'it' when they played tag, and his long floppy toes prevented him from ever catching anyone.

Alfred began trying different ways to keep his shoes properly curled. He tied them with strings but the strings broke. One night he wrapped them around hair curlers and fastened them with hair-grips. But as soon as he took the curlers out, the toes straightened.

Alfred even tried hair spray and liquid starch. Each worked for a short time, but soon the toes would come uncurled.

The other elves no longer played with him. They didn't ask him to join their singing. They didn't help him with his work. They left him alone.

So here Alfred sat alone, with his shoes in his lap. Their long toes did not have even the slightest wave in them. Alfred looked around the empty workshop. He looked at all the wonderful toys stacked on the shelves. Then he looked at the toys he had made. The Chief Inspector had placed them on the bottom shelf – out of sight.

There was the lion with zebra stripes, a hippopotamus with an elephant's trunk, a giraffe with a short neck, and a teddy bear with a cross-eyed stare!

'Poor sad children,' Alfred thought. 'Poor little children who are wishing for a toy animal that is just right. How disappointed they will be on Christmas morning. If only I hadn't been in such a hurry to make my animals.'

Alfred began to remember all the other toys that had not turned out right. Then he wondered, 'Could it be that my shoes uncurl because I am careless with my work?' Alfred decided he would find out.

The next day he took two big safety-pins and pinned the toes of his shoes out of the way. Then he went to the workroom with the other elves. One by one he took the mixed-up animals and made them right again.

First, he gave the lion got a proper coat. Then he removed the elephant's trunk from the hippopotamus. He stretched the giraffe's neck and adjusted the eyes of the cross-eyed bear so that they looked straight ahead. Each day Alfred made a stuffed toy slowly and carefully and made sure that they were just right. No longer did the Chief Inspector shake his head and put Alfred's toys on the bottom shelf.

It was now so close to Christmas that the elves did not have time to play. They worked and worked to fill all the shelves ready for Father Christmas's trip. They did not sing or tell riddles. Everyone was too busy to notice Alfred's work or to tease him about his shoes.

The safety-pins still held the toes of his shoes so that they were curled back. Each night Alfred tightened them up, repinned them and set them beside his bed.

On Christmas Eve all the toys were finally loaded into Father Christmas's sleigh. Away went Father Christmas and the reindeer for the long night's trip around the world.

The elves waved and cheered until he was out of sight. Then they rushed back into the empty workroom to sing and dance and play elf games and to eat biscuits and drink milk.

Alfred sat by himself on one of the benches until one of the elves tagged him and said 'Hi, Alfred. You're it for a game of tag.'

Alfred hesitated. But then he remembered the big safety-pins that held the toes of his shoes in place. He ran here and there tagging this elf and that, until finally all the elves had been tagged.

They sat in a great circle around Alfred and applauded because he had been such a good 'it'.

Alfred sat down in the middle of the circle to catch his breath. It was then that he discovered the safety-pins were no longer in his shoes. And yet his shoes curled up tight as a spring! From then on Alfred worked carefully and never had problems with his shoes.

Today Alfred's toys are so well made that he has become a chief inspector himself. But over his bed still hang two very large safety-pins to remind him what careless work did to a little elf's shoes.

Annabelle Sumera

# Henry's Christmas ear-muffs

Henry Greymouse simply hated winter weather. From November through to March he felt shivery and just plain miserable. His ears, in particular, were sensitive to cold. Most of the time they felt like two icebergs perched on top of his head.

Whenever he complained to his wife, Mabel, she said, 'It's because you're not as young as you used to be, Henry. When a mouse gets on in years, it's only natural that he should feel the cold more.'

What Mabel said made sense. But still, Henry could not see why he had to put up with chilly ears. People didn't.

So one autumn Henry decided to make himself some ear-muffs. He found just what he needed, down in Murky Hollow. What he found were two pearly mushrooms about the size of clover blossoms. When Henry tied them together with a bit of marsh reed they nestled cosily over his ears.

'Beautiful!' he smiled. 'I'll give them to myself for a Christmas present. Christmas is just about the time when the wintry snow begins to fly.'

Henry took the ear-muffs home. He gift-wrapped them in some silvery chewing-gum paper he had found near a farm house. Then he stowed them away in the cupboard.

The weeks marched by. Just as Henry had predicted, the Greymice woke up to a white Christmas. As they ate their holiday breakfast of wheat tassels and sugar lumps, it gave Henry great pleasure to think of those nice warm ear-muffs waiting for him under the Christmas tree.

When the last sugar lump had gone, the Greymice opened their presents. Henry gave Mabel a milkweed-down pillow and some rose petal dusting powder. Mabel gave Henry a cherry-wood walking stick and a packet of

corn crackles. They were both very pleased with their presents. Then Henry unwrapped his ear-muffs and ceremoniously put them on. Mabel stared at him in astonishment. 'Goodness gracious, Henry!' she cried. 'Your ears look as though they are sprouting toadstools!'

'They're mushroom ear-muffs!' Henry replied indignantly. 'I made them last autumn as a Christmas present to myself. Lucky thing, too. I've never seen a more wintry-looking Christmas. My ears will keep snug and warm when I'm out shovelling snow.'

'Henry, you are the oddest mouse I know,' sighed Mabel. 'You don't give presents to yourself. It just isn't done. You'll be the laughing-stock of Mouse Town. Only people wear ear-muffs.'

'This mouse does, too.' said Henry. He stomped outside to dig a path through the snow. The wind howled, the snow blew, and icicles cracked and snapped. Henry's ears stayed as warm as two peach buds in spring. He couldn't remember when he'd felt so happy on a cold winter's day.

Pretty soon the neighbours began to gather round. They thought Henry's ear-muffs were the funniest things they'd seen in years. They laughed and hooted. Some of them rolled in the snow laughing. Grandpa Fieldmouse chuckled so hard that he swallowed the piece of pine gum he had received for Christmas.

Henry let none of this bother him. He just carried on digging and humming happily, because his ears were so toasty under the mushrooms.

However, when he went back into the kitchen he found that Mabel was not so happy. She was muttering under her breath as she made preparations for Christmas dinner.

'What's the matter?' asked Henry.

'Matter!' cried Mabel. 'It's just as I predicted. You're the laughing stock of Mouse Town, that's what!'

'Who cares?' he said.

'I care!' Mabel squeaked.

She went on to say she'd never be able to hold her head up in Mouse Town if he insisted on wearing mushrooms over his ears.

She complained so long and loudly that Henry put on his ear-muffs again. To his delight, the ear-muffs shut out most of what Mabel was saying. There and then he decided to wear them all the time. Not only did they keep his ears warm, but they also made the world seem nicely muffled and peaceful.

Mabel, alas, grew unhappier by the day. It was no fun living with a husband who could not hear what you said and who was the laughing stock of the town besides. Often she would lift one of Henry's ear-muffs and shout, 'Those good-for-nothing mushrooms! I wish you'd never found them!'

Henry felt sorry that Mabel disliked his ear-muffs. He thought they were the most wonderful thing a mouse had ever invented, and the best Christmas present he'd ever had.

Then, on New Year's Eve, Mabel lifted an ear-muff and said, 'Listen, Henry. There's terrible news! Mayor Meadowmouse's dear daughter Brenda has a bad case of speckle-spots! The poor little tot is not expected to recover. It's such a sad thing to happen.'

Henry was very fond of little Brenda. He yanked off his ear-muffs so he could hear more.

'Why isn't she expected to get well?'

'Because she has lost her appetite and won't eat anything. They have tried to get her to eat oatmeal, corn-mush, and barley gruel. But she'll have none of it. She's just wasting away to a shadow.'

'I don't wonder,' Henry observed. 'All that is such plain fare. Sick mice need dainty little delicacies to tempt their run down appetites.'

'I know,' Mabel agreed. 'But we mice never have dainty little titbits in winter. At this time of the year all we have left is plain hearty grain.'

For a while Henry and Mabel sat grieving about poor Brenda Meadowmouse. Then, all at once Henry popped up. He grabbed his ear-muffs and began chopping them up into a cooking pot.

'What in the world are you doing, Henry?' Mabel asked.

'I'm making *mushroom à la kingmouse*,' he replied. 'If that doesn't tempt Brenda, I don't know what will.'

'What a generous thing to do!' cried Mabel. 'I know how fond you are of those ear-muffs. It could not have been easy for you to toss them into the cooking pot.'

'Oh, never mind,' he said. 'Somehow sharing my Christmas ear-muffs with Brenda makes me feel Christmassy all over again.'

Very shortly, Henry and Mabel carried a tempting bowl of *mushroom à la kingmouse* over to the Meadowmouse house. Little Brenda found it so delicious that she ate the entire bowl. By the next day she was feeling so much better that she ate corn-mush and barley gruel.

That evening as the Greymice sat by the fire, Mabel said, 'You're quite the hero, Henry. Everyone says that your mushrooms saved Brenda's life. How lucky it was that you made those ear-muffs last autumn. You're a very clever and resourceful mouse.'

'I'm happy you feel that way,' said Henry. He was very glad indeed. For he was already planning to make himself new ear-muffs for next Christmas. He was planning some for his neighbours and maybe Mabel, too. And he thought he'd whip up a few extra pairs, just in case any mice come down with the speckle-spots!

Frances B. Watts

# The great Christmas mix-up

One Saturday afternoon, Kevin and his mum went down the High Street to do their Christmas shopping.

Kevin spotted a black leather jacket with studs on.

'Get that for Spike, Mum,' he said. 'He'd love it.'

Mum saw a soft cosy rug.

'Just right for Gran,' she said, 'when she's sitting watching telly in the evenings.'

Kevin found a blue teddy with a ribbon. It had googly eyes that wobbled when you shook it.

'Katie will like this,' said Kevin. 'She must be tired of that fluffy rabbit of hers.'

Mum picked out a pair of slippers for Dad.

'Fully lined and going half price,' she said. 'Much better than those awful old things he wears all the time.'

'How about this for Waffles?' said Kevin, holding up a lead. 'He's chewed his old one to bits.'

'Good idea,' said Mum. 'Now, Kevin, you look at this nice pile of books for a minute. I've got something to do in the music department.'

Kevin smiled to himself. He knew what Mum was up to. She was buying a present for him and she didn't want him to watch. He looked at the books for a moment, but then something shiny on the next stand caught his eye. It was a row of kitchen utensils and right at the front, all bright and sparkling, was a lovely metal egg whisk with a scarlet handle. It was like the one he usually borrowed to make bubbles in the bath, only it was bigger, and brighter, and better.

Quick as a wink, Kevin pulled it off the hook and ran to the woman at the till.

'I want this please,' he said in a loud whisper. 'It's for my mum.'

The woman smiled at him.

'Have you got any money?' she said.

Kevin pulled some money out of his pocket. He'd been saving up for weeks to do his Christmas shopping. The lady picked out two pound coins and one fifty pence coin and wrapped the egg whisk in a paper bag.

'There you are dear,' she said. 'Be careful, mind, and don't get your fingers caught in it.'

On Christmas Eve, Kevin and Mum wrapped up all their Christmas presents and put them under the Christmas tree. The pile looked beautiful; all mysterious, and crackly, and exciting. They were just standing back to admire the effect when the door burst open. In came Spike and Waffles.

Suddenly, everything happened at once. Waffles saw the parcels and made a dash at them. He started chewing the paper off. Spike let out a howl and made a dash at Waffles. He knocked the Christmas tree over. Mum shrieked and grabbed the Christmas tree. She just managed to catch it in time. Kevin nearly burst into tears.

'It's all right,' said Spike, when he'd got hold of Waffles. 'Just you leave it to me. You two take Waffles off into the kitchen, and I'll clear it all up.'

When Kevin went back into the sitting room, Spike had nearly finished. He was looking very pleased with himself.

'Looks smashing, doesn't it?' he said to Kevin.

Kevin nodded. Spike was right. It did look very nice, but somehow things weren't quite the same. There was something about the Christmas tree... and then some of the parcels seemed to have changed their shape....

On Christmas morning, the great moment came. Everyone gave presents to everyone else. Kevin got some LEGO, and a suit of armour, and a book, and a puzzle, and a beautiful garage with cars that fitted neatly inside it. Spike got a set of new mirrors for his motorbike, Gran got a book of knitting patterns, Mum got a box of her favourite chocolates, and Dad got some funny socks.

'Here,' said Spike, when the floor was already deep in wrapping paper. 'We forgot these ones under the tree. Look Gran here's one for you.'

Gran quickly ripped off the paper, and pulled her present out.

'Oh!' she said. 'A leather jacket! With studs on! Just what I've always wanted. It'll keep the wind off me when I'm fishing.'

Spike got his next.

'Hey!' he said. 'What a nice little ted! Real cool eyes. It'll be my mascot. Thanks Mum.'

Then it was Dad's turn.

'A rug!' he said, when he'd opened his present. 'Just what I need when I'm out bird-watching. I nearly froze to death last week.'

Katie had been trying to open her parcel for ages. She couldn't get the paper off. Gran had to help her.

'Nice string! Nice string! she said, when she got the dog's lead out at last. She was so happy, she dribbled. She carefully looped it round the funnel of her train, and started pulling it round the room.

'Choo! Choo! Choo!' she said.

Waffles had helped himself to his present. Dad was the first to notice him.

'Here, that's a good idea,' he said, 'giving Waffles a pair of slippers of his own. Now perhaps he'll leave my nice old ones alone.'

Mum and Kevin looked at each other and laughed.

'I think we'd better open ours now, don't you? she said. She got the paper off first. Inside was a cassette of pop music.

'It's a good thing we both like the same groups, isn't it Kevin?' she said. 'This'll keep me company when I'm washing the car.

Kevin was too happy to answer her. He was looking at the whisk, his whisk. He'd play with it in the bath that very night. It would make the biggest, the best, the most beautiful bubbles he had ever seen. And it was his very own.

Elizabeth Laird

# Christmas trees and decorations

Before Christianity came to Europe, most people believed in the Druid religion. Druids worshipped the gods of light and darkness. They believed that light and darkness fought a constant battle in the sky. Sometimes light won, and the sun shone. Sometimes darkness won, and the sun hid.

Every year, Druids believed, darkness was strongest in wintertime. The nights were long. The weather was cold. Nothing could grow. Light still ruled for a few hours each day, but it was feeble and struggled to survive. It needed human help if spring and warmth were ever to come again.

One way to help light, people believed, was to take an evergreen tree inside your house. You kept it growing there in the dark, cold days. On 25 December, the birthday of the god of light, you decorated it with candles. People thought that if everyone did this in every house, the god of light would gradually grow stronger. The days would grow longer and the nights shorter. Spring would be on its way.

When Christmas came to Europe, the Europeans took over this festival of light. The Bible calls Jesus 'the Light of the World' – and it seemed a good idea to celebrate his birthday on 25 December, the day of the old light festival. (No one knows the actual day of Jesus's birth. Two thousand years ago, in Roman times, people made little fuss about birthdays.)

That's how the idea of Christmas trees began. In northern countries most people use fir trees, because firs keep their greenness even in the coldest weather. In warmer countries people use other kinds of trees. Nut trees and fruit trees (oranges or lemons) are favourites.

We still keep the custom of decorating our trees. The main decoration, just as it was in Druid times, is candles (or nowadays, coloured lightbulbs). Their glow shows that Christmas is a festival of light, of Jesus, Light of the World. On top of the tree people once used to put a doll, a model of the baby Jesus. Then it was changed to an angel – and from that to a Christmas fairy, with a silken dress and a magic wand.

We hang other decorations on the tree. There are bright-coloured globes and balls of glass. They dangle from the branches like unusual fruit. In the old days, people used *real* fruit. Instead of glass globes, they hung oranges, pears and apples from the branches, and added pine cones, sometimes painted gold or silver.

Sometimes we hang small presents wrapped in Christmas paper on the branches of the tree. There may also

be sweets or chocolates. In Germany and Sweden, there may be biscuits or gingerbread.

Another decoration for the Christmas tree is tinsel. This is made from thin, silver strips. Some strips are straight. Others are furry and fuzzy, like threads of fluffed-out wool. Tinsel can be other colours; gold, violet, green. But it's usually silver – and an old story tells the reason why.

The story is about the time when Jesus was a baby. The King of his country had heard that a child had recently been born who would grow up to be King of Kings. His majesty was frightened that the new King might steal his throne. He ordered his soldiers to hunt down all male children under the age of four, and kill them. Mary and Joseph took Jesus, their son, and fled. They hoped to find safety in Egypt.

For a while, all went well. But the soldiers had horses, and Joseph and Mary were on foot. They could not escape forever. As they hurried along, they could hear the sound of hooves in the distance behind them, the wailing of mothers and children, and the officers shouting orders to their men. Joseph said to Mary, 'It's getting dark. We're exhausted. We must find somewhere to shelter for the night.'

'It's useless,' Mary said. 'They're searching everywhere. They're sure to find us.'

Joseph said, 'We'll still try. We'll pray to God for help.'

Joseph and Mary found a cave, and hid in the dark inside. Mary cradled baby Jesus in her cloak. She and Joseph lay down on the rocky ground to sleep as best they could.

All night the soldiers searched. It was frosty and cold. They galloped through the undergrowth, slashing the trees with their swords in case anyone was hiding in the branches. They checked every hollow, every ditch, every hiding place they could find.

At dawn they came to the cave where Joseph and Mary were hiding. 'Shall we try this one, sir?' the soldiers asked.

'No,' said the officer. 'Look, the entrance is covered. Nothing's disturbed it. They can't be there.' So the soldiers went away, and Mary, Joseph and Jesus were safe.

What had saved them? While Mary and Joseph were asleep, spiders had spun webs and lines across the cave-mouth. Then, in the night, frost had covered the webs. They hung there like a curtain of silver threads, glistening and glittering in the morning sun. They kept Mary, Joseph and baby Jesus safe.

That's the story – and people say that's why we hang tinsel on our Christmas trees.

The hanging up of mistletoe is another custom that goes back to Druid times. You gather mistletoe and hang it overhead, in the middle of a room or in a doorway. Every girl who passes underneath it has to kiss the nearest boy, and every boy has to kiss the nearest girl. Some people enjoy this a lot; others are embarrassed. It must have been more embarrassing in Druid times. Then, if no one kissed you, people believed you would never marry. And if you weren't kissed twelve times in one evening, it meant very bad luck indeed!

Kenneth McLeish

# Shake, rattle and roll

Hallo, my name is Glub and I'm a guinea pig. I live at Tinbury Primary School and I'm going to tell you what happened when I went to stay with Ben Bingley for my Christmas holidays. I wasn't sure what happened at 'Christmas'. I only knew that it must be important because the children in school had been talking about it for weeks.

Well, Mrs Bingley had hardly got my hutch through the back door when Sarah, Ben's sister, said, 'Block your ears Ben.' Then she whispered to me, 'Guess what I've got Ben for Christmas, Glub – a huge box of Maltesers and a giant tube of Smarties. Don't tell him, it's a secret.'

A few days later Ben took me out of my hutch and said, 'I've got a jigsaw for Sarah for Christmas – only you mustn't tell her. It's a secret.'

'Well,' I thought, 'All these secrets are very strange.' But I kept quiet.

The next day Ben's family seemed to go slightly mad. They started hanging coloured paper from the ceiling and dangling picture cards on ribbons down the walls. But the maddest thing of all that they did – and you're not going to believe this – was to bring a tree into the sitting room and start hanging little balls and lights all over it, and a shiny gold star on the top. I tell you, I lay on my back in that cage, legs in the air, laughing my head off. I mean trees don't grow indoors, do they?

That night, when Sarah and Ben had gone to bed, Mrs Bingley took a very large cake out of its even larger tin, and started spreading white stuff all over it.

'Yum, yum,' said Mr Bingley, licking a bit of the white stuff and winking at me. 'You should taste this, Glub,' he went on, 'best Christmas cake I've ever tasted.'

'Well, give us a bit,' I thought, but I was out of luck.

'Hey Glub,' said Mrs Bingley. 'We didn't tell you what we've got Ben for Christmas, did we? We've got him a racing car.'

'But don't worry, we haven't forgotten you,' said Mr Bingley. 'There's something for you too, Glub.'

That night I was far too excited to sleep so I jiggled the catch on my hutch until the door opened and I sneaked out.

The moon was shining in through the sitting room window and what a glorious sight met my eyes. There at the bottom of that indoor tree were lots and lots of brightly coloured packages.

'This is pretty,' I thought and ran to explore them. 'And great fun for running and rolling over.' Oops! One of my claws got stuck, and the more I tottered and turned, the more the paper tore, leaving long strips all over the rug. Then out of the paper fell a rattly box.

'This looks interesting,' I thought. So I chewed through the box and lots of little dark brown balls rolled out. I nibbled one and it tasted delicious! I nibbled some of the other balls. I also found that they were just right for playing football with. Wee, I kicked one under the table. 'Goal!' I shouted as I kicked one under the curtains. Little balls were soon scattered all over the room.

Then I spotted some silver paper covered with little fat men, with long white beards and great red cloaks. The paper made an interesting crinkly, crackly noise as I ripped it off. There was a big flat box inside. It didn't take me long to chew and nibble through the box. And inside were lots of brightly coloured wooden shapes. I didn't think that these would taste as delicious as the little brown balls and so I started to pull the paper off a long rattly tube-shaped package. After tugging with my teeth and a touch of shake, rattle and roll, out came lots of little coloured button shapes. These tasted every bit as good as the balls. When I'd nibbled enough of these I noticed a gleaming purple package. I was dying to know what was inside. So... rip, rip, claw, claw, tear, tear, pieces of purple paper were scattered everywhere. I gasped when I saw what was inside. It was a shiny new red car. It was wonderful!

But this can't be Ben's car. It's far too small for Ben. His mum and dad must have made a mistake. Then I remembered what Mr Bingley had said. He said there was something for ME! This must be it. It was just the right size!

I started to stroke the car and it started to whirr.... I climbed on to it. I liked the whirring noise. 'Come on car,' I said, 'Let's get going.' And suddenly we did! Off we went whizzing round the room.

It was brilliant! We zoomed and bumped all over the purple paper, the balls, the wood shapes and the tasty buttons. Round and round we whirled, dodging here and there, roaring round the tree, bashing into the door, under the table and out the other side, round and round and round and round... until I was so dizzy I toppled off, and the car stopped whirring and lay on its side.

'What a wonderful car,' I thought.

I was very, very tired and I must have fallen asleep right there and then, because the next thing I heard was, 'Happy Christmas!' 'Happy Christmas, Ben.' 'Happy Christmas, Glub....'

Then there was silence.

I opened one eye then the other. Was it morning already? Ben's family were all standing there. They were standing quite still, their eyes were round and their mouths were open.

'That's the jigsaw puzzle that I got for Sarah,' Ben said sadly.

'And those are the Smarties and Maltesers I got for Ben,' Sarah said very softly.

'Glub, you naughty guinea pig! You've spoilt all our presents,' said Ben's mum.

'What an awful mess,' they all said together.

I began to feel a bit ashamed. I must have done something terribly naughty. How could I make them all cheer up? Perhaps if they saw how pleased I was with my new car, they'd feel better.

I jumped on to the car again and in no time we were whizzing round and round the room just as before. I whistled away happily.

Mr and Mrs Bingley began to smile, then Sarah grinned and began to giggle. Soon the whole family started to laugh.

'Oh Glub,' spluttered Ben's dad, 'did you think that the car was *your* present?'

I leapt off the car in surprise.

'This is your present,' said Ben's mum, giving me the biggest carrot I'd ever seen. And that made them all start laughing again.

Ann Bryant

# Father Christmas and Father Christmas

Jeremy James first met Father Christmas one Saturday morning in a big shop. He was a little surprised to see him there, because it was soon going to be Christmas, and Jeremy James thought Santa Claus really ought to be somewhere in the North Pole filling sacks with presents and feeding his reindeer. However, there he was, on a platform in the toy department, handing out little parcels to the boys and girls who came to see him.

'Here you are, Jeremy James,' said Daddy, and handed him a 50p piece.

'What's that for?' asked Jeremy James.

'To give to Santa Claus,' said Daddy. 'You have to pay to go and see him. I'll wait for you here.'

Daddy stood rocking the twins in the pram, while Jeremy James joined the end of a long queue of children (Mummy was busy wasting time in the food department.) Jeremy James thought it rather odd that you had to pay for Santa Claus. It was if Santa Claus was a bar of chocolate or a packet of liquorice all-sorts.

'Do we really have to pay 50p to see him?' he asked a tall boy in front of him.

'Yeah,' said the tall boy, 'An' he'll prob'ly give you a plastic car worth 5p.'

Jeremy James stood on tiptoe to try and catch a glimpse of Father Christmas. He could just see him, all wrapped up in his red cloak and hood, talking to a little girl with pigtails. It certainly was him – there was no mistaking the long white beard and the rosy cheeks. It was really quite an honour that Santa Claus should have come to this particular shop out of all the shops in the world, and perhaps he needed the 50p to pay for his long journey. Jeremy James looked across towards his Daddy, and they gave each other a cheery wave.

As Jeremy James drew closer to Santa Claus, he felt more and more excited. Santa Claus seemed such a nice man. He was talking to each of the children before he gave them their present, and he would pat them on the head and sometimes let out a jolly laugh, and only once did he seem at all un-Father-Christmas-like; that was when a ginger-haired boy with freckles stepped up before him and said he hadn't got 50p but he wanted a present all the same. Then Father Christmas pulled a very serious face and Jeremy James distinctly heard him ask the boy if he'd like a thick ear, which seemed a strange sort of present to offer. The boy wandered off grumbling, and when he was some distance away stuck his tongue out at Santa Claus, but by then the next child was on the platform and the jolly smile had returned as he reached out for the 50p piece.

Jeremy James noticed, with a slight twinge of disappointment that the presents really were rather small, but as Santa Claus had had to bring so many, perhaps he simply hadn't had room for bigger ones. It was still quite exciting to look at the different shapes and the different wrappings and try to guess what was inside them, and by the time Jeremy James came face to face with the great man, his eyes were shining and his heart thumping with anticipation.

'What's your name?' asked Santa Claus in a surprisingly young voice.

'Jeremy James,' said Jeremy James.

'And have you got 50p for Santa Claus?'

'Yes,' said Jeremy James, handing it over.

Then Santa Claus gave a big smile, and his blue eyes twinkled out from below his bushy white eyebrows, and Jeremy James could see his shining white teeth between the bushy white moustache and the bushy white beard. All the bushy whiteness looked remarkably like cotton wool, and the redness on the cheeks looked remarkably like red paint, which made Jeremy James feel that Santa Claus really was very different to everybody else he knew.

'Is it for your reindeer?' asked Jeremy James.

'What?' asked Santa Claus.

'The 50p,' said Jeremy James.

'Ah,' said Santa Claus, 'ah well... in a kind of sort of a manner of speaking as you might say. Now then Jeremy James, what do you want for Father Christmas?'

Oh, I'd like a tricycle, with a bell *and* a saddlebag. Gosh, is that what you're going to give me?'

'Ah no, not exactly,' said Santa Claus, 'not now anyway. Not for 50p matey. But here's a little something to keep you going.'

And Santa Claus handed him a little oblong packet wrapped in Father-Christmassy paper.

'Thank you,' said Jeremy James. 'And do you really live in the North Pole?'

'Feels like it sometimes,' said Santa Claus. 'My landlord never heats the bedrooms. Off you go. Next!'

Jeremy James carried his little packet across to where Mummy had joined Daddy to wait with the twins.

'Open it up then,' said Daddy.

Jeremy James opened it up. It was a little box. And inside the little box was a plastic car.

'Worth at least 2p,' said Daddy.

'Five,' said Jeremy James.

Jeremy James's second meeting with Santa Claus came a week and a day later. It was at a children's party in the church hall. The party began with the Reverend Cole hobbling on to the platform and saying several times in his creaky voice that he hoped everyone would enjoy himself, and the party was to end with Santa Claus coming and giving out the presents. In between, there were games, eating and drinking, and more games. As soon as the first lot of games got underway, the Reverend Cole hobbled out of the hall, and nobody even noticed that he'd gone. The games were very noisy and full of running around, he enjoyed himself.

The eating and drinking bit came next, and Jeremy James showed that he was just as good at eating and drinking as he was at making a noise and running around. In fact Mummy, who was one of the helpers (having left Daddy at home to mind the twins and the television set), actually stopped him when he was on the verge of breaking the world record for the number of mince pies eaten at a single go. When at last there was not a crumb left on any of the tables, the helpers cleared the empty paper plates and the empty paper cups and the not so empty wooden floor. After a few more games full of shrieks and squeaks and bumps and thumps, all the children had completely forgotten them. At the stroke of six o'clock, one of the grown-ups called for everyone to keep quiet and stand still, and at ten past six, when everyone was quiet and standing still, the hall door opened, and in came Father Christmas.

The first thing Jeremy James noticed about Father Christmas was how slowly he walked – as if his body was very heavy and his legs very weak. He was wearing the same red coat and hood as before, and he had a white beard and moustache, but... somehow they were not nearly as bushy. His cheeks were nice and red, but... he was wearing a pair of spectacles. And when he called out to the children: 'Merry Christmas, everyone, and I hope you're enjoying yourselves!' his voice was surprisingly creaky and hollow-sounding.

Jeremy James frowned as Santa Claus heaved himself and his sack up on to the platform. There was definitely something strange about him. The other children didn't seem to notice, and they were all excited as the helpers made them line up, but perhaps the others had never met Santa Claus before, so how could they know?

Jeremy James patiently waited for his turn, and when it came, he stepped confidently up on to the platform.

'Now... we... what's your name?' said Santa Claus, peering down at Jeremy James.

'You should remember,' said Jeremy James. 'It was only a week ago that I told you.'

'Oh, dear,' said Santa Claus. 'I do have a terrible memory.'

'And a week ago,' said Jeremy James, 'you weren't wearing glasses, and your voice wasn't all creaky like it is now.'

'Oh,' said Santa Claus, 'wasn't I... er... wasn't it?'

Jeremy James looked very carefully at Santa Claus's face, and Santa Claus looked back at Jeremy James with a rather puzzled expression in his... brown eyes.

'Santa Claus has blue eyes! said Jeremy James.

'Oh!' said Santa Claus, his mouth dropping open in surprise.

'And he's got white teeth, too!' said Jeremy James.

'Hm!' said Santa Claus, closing his mouth in dismay.

'You're not Santa Claus at all,' said Jeremy James. 'You're not!'

And so saying, Jeremy James turned to the whole crowd of children and grown-ups, and announced at the top of his voice:

'He's a cheat! He's not Father Christmas!'

Father Christmas rose unsteadily to his feet, and as he did so, his hood feel off, revealing a shining bald head. Father Christmas hastily raised a hand to pull the hood back on, but his hand brushed against his beard and knocked it sideways, and as he tried to save his beard, he brushed against his moustache, and that fell off altogether, revealing beneath it the face of... the Reverend Cole.

'There!' said Jeremy James. 'That proves it!'

One or two of the children started crying, but then the man who had been organising the games jumped up on to the platform and explained that the real Santa Claus was very busy preparing for Christmas, and that was why the Reverend Cole had had to take his place. They hadn't wanted to disappoint the children. And it was just bad luck that there'd been such a clever little boy at the party, but the clever little boy should be congratulated all the same on being so clever, and if they could just go on pretending that the Reverend Cole was the real Santa Claus, the clever little boy should have two presents as a special reward for being so clever.

Then the Reverend Cole put on his beard and his moustache and hood again, and everybody clapped very loudly as Jeremy James collected his two presents. And they were big presents too, a book of Bible stories, and a set of paints and brushes. As Jeremy James said to Mummy on the way home:

'It's funny that the real Santa Claus only gave me a rotten old car for 50p, but Mr Cole gave me these big presents for nothing.'

But as Father Christmas was a grown-up, and the Reverend Cole was also a grown up, Jeremy James knew there was no point in trying to understand it at all. Grown-ups never behave the way you'd expect them to.

David Henry Wilson

# A troublesome year for Father Christmas

One year nothing went right for Father Christmas. To begin with, the mice had been nibbling at his sacks, so they were full of holes and the toys fell through. Then he found that the elves had been growing geraniums in his Christmas-best boots. The elf children had used up all his notepads for colouring, so he hadn't any paper to write thank you notes to people who left him mince pies. And when he jumped into his sleigh, he slid on an egg that one of his hens laid there.

He finally set off an hour late and with the grumbles of his reindeer ringing in his ears. They all had colds and were feeling very sorry for themselves. Father Christmas had to make them fly faster than usual to make up for lost time. He didn't dare think about what would happen if he hadn't visited every child throughout the world before morning.

They sped through the air, bells ringing loudly, and reached the first houses in double-quick time. Father Christmas slid down the chimneys like a fireman down his pole, and filled every stocking lying alongside every sleeping child. Then off they went again, to the next village, the next town, the next city, on and on until....

Rudolph's nose went out. Suddenly it was very, very dark. They were in the middle of nowhere and there were no lights from the ground to guide them. The reindeer came to a halt.

'What's the matter Rudolph?' said Father Christmas.

'It's dis cold in me dose,' said Rudolph. 'It's made me dose stop shining.'

'Bother my boots,' said Father Christmas. 'Bother my belt and braces.' He fiddled around at the front of the sleigh and found a small torch. When he switched it on, a thin line of light streamed out in front of him.

'Bother my beard,' said Father Christmas. 'This is all the light we've got, and it won't last long. There's only one thing for it, we'll have to wake up the Man in the Moon.'

As soon as he said it a loud groan came from all the reindeer. It was bad

enough flying around the world with a bad cold, let alone paying a visit to the Man in the Moon on the way. Besides, he always looked so grumpy.

'Come on now,' said Father Christmas. 'We must get going. We're late enough already.'

He steered the sleigh away from the Earth and up, up, up they flew, the thin light from the torch guiding them towards the very faint circle in the distance. It didn't take long. It was much quicker to go to the moon than travel all the way round the Earth. When they reached the landing platform, Father Christmas tumbled out and ran to the Man in the Moon's front door. He knocked loudly. There was no reply. He knocked again. Still no reply. A loud rumbly snore echoed around the Man in the Moon's house.

'Bother my bootlaces,' said Father Christmas. 'We'll never wake him up.'

The reindeer stood miserably sniffing and shuffling their feet.

'Come on now, reindeer,' said Father Christmas. 'I want you all to stamp your hooves, whinny as loudly as you can, and dance around to make your bells ring.'

'But what about our sore throats?' protested Rudolph.

'Never mind your sore throats,' said Father Christmas. 'This is an emergency!'

The reindeer did as they were told. The noise was tremendous. Father Christmas joined in by going HO HO HO! as loudly as he could and blowing the horn on the sleigh.

Suddenly a light went on somewhere in the house, and a grumpy voice bellowed through the letter-box. 'What's going on? Who the dickens is making all that racket? Who dares to wake me up on one of my few days off? Speak up!'

'I'm terribly sorry,' said Father Christmas, 'but we need your help. I'm Father Christmas and I'm on my way around the world delivering presents. But Rudolph's shiny nose has gone out and we can't see where we're going.'

The door of the house opened and a huge, bad-tempered man appeared. 'I suppose you want me to work, do you?' said the Man in the Moon. 'You come here and wake me up with all your racket, and now you want me to work. Why should I?'

Father Christmas took a deep breath and the reindeer tossed their heads uneasily. 'A lot of children will be very unhappy if they wake up to empty stockings tomorrow morning,' said Father Christmas.

'Nobody ever gave me a present,' grumbled the Man in the Moon. 'Never. Not even a Christmas card. I hate Christmas. That's why I always sleep on Christmas Eve instead of working.'

Father Christmas listened sympathetically, and then he had an idea. 'I tell you what,' he said. 'I'll bring you presents. I'll come here with my reindeer every year after we've been around the world, and we'll eat mince pies and talk and you can open presents in front of the fire. But in return you must promise always to work on Christmas Eve so that I'll always be able to find my way.'

Try as he might to keep on his grumpy face, a twinkle appeared in the Man in the Moon's eye.

'Do you mean it?' he said.

'Go to work now,' said Father Christmas, 'and I'll join you for breakfast in the morning and give you your presents.'

The Man in the Moon disappeared indoors without another word. Suddenly, the whole place was bathed in bright light. The reindeer screwed up their eyes, half-blinded. Father Christmas jumped back into his sleigh.

'Come on', he said. 'Full speed ahead. No time to lose.'

And off they went, down, down, down, until they could see the tops of the trees and buildings again. When Father Christmas looked back, there was the Moon shining brightly, and there was the face of the Man in the Moon smiling broadly.

Father Christmas just managed to finish delivering presents on time that year. Then he went back to the Moon and shared mince pies and brandy with the Man in the Moon and left him his presents. He finally arrived back at the North Pole at lunchtime on Christmas Day. He sent his reindeer off to a health farm for a week, and settled down for a nice long sleep.

The Man in the Moon always works on Christmas Eve now and, as you will see, he has a smile on his face all the year around.

Sally Grindley

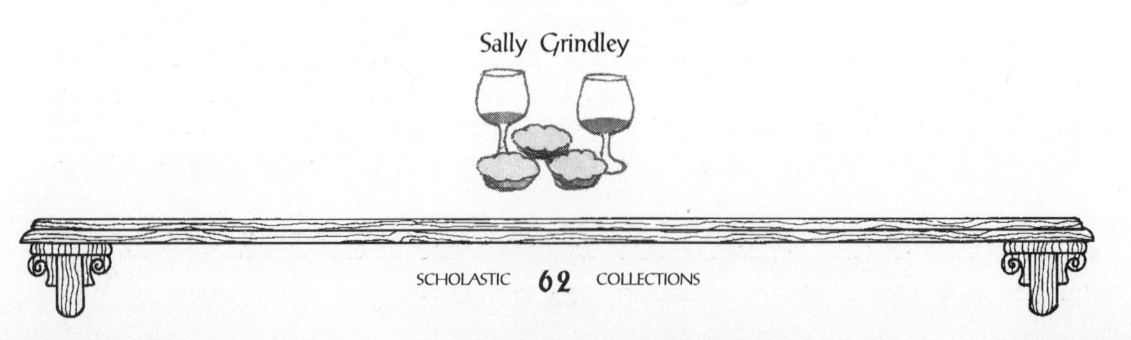

# Santa Claus

Round about Christmas, in many families, arguments about Santa Claus begin. 'He doesn't exist!' 'He does!' 'He doesn't!'

Well, in a way he does. Hundreds of years ago, in the country which is now Turkey, there was a Christian bishop called Nicholas. He was a rich and powerful man, a prince of the church. He travelled about the country, visiting churches, baptising people, talking and preaching about religion.

Nicholas was popular. Everyone loved him. After he died, they told stories about how he had helped people. These stories reached the ears of the Pope in Rome. He declared that Nicholas was to be honoured as Saint Nicholas for evermore.

How did Saint Nicholas help people? These are the kinds of stories his admirers told. Once he was sailing, far out to sea, when a storm began. Waves towered, wind roared, the sailors staggered about the deck and howled. Nicholas put on his bishop's cloak and his tall, pointed hat. He stood on deck and prayed to God. At once the wind stopped, the waves died – and when the sailors opened their eyes the sea was as calm as glass.

Another, more gruesome story tells about Saint Nicholas and the Pickled Boys. Once, the story says, three princes stayed the night at a country inn. The innkeeper saw their rich clothes, their jewels and their money-bags. He waited till dark, then murdered the boys and locked their clothes and jewels in a cupboard. Then he sliced the bodies into steaks, chops and rashers, and stored them in barrels filled with salt, to pickle them for winter. Not long afterwards, Saint Nicholas stayed at the inn. He had a dream telling him what had happened. He prayed to God, and the three boys jumped out of the barrels, whole and healthy, singing 'Praise be to God' while the innkeeper stood and gaped.

The last Saint Nicholas story explains his connection with Christmas. Once, the story goes, a poor man had three daughters. They grew up, and it was time for the eldest to marry. But in those days, when a woman married, her father had to give her new husband a dowry a present of goods or money. This father was too poor. He had no dowry to give. No man was interested in marrying his daughter. One night, the daughter washed her stockings before she went to bed, and hung them to dry by the open window. Next morning, when she tried to put the stockings on, she found a bag of gold coins in one of the toes. She used the coins as a dowry, and so was able to marry. The same thing happened with the second daughter. When it was the third daughter's turn, the father decided to find out where the mysterious gold was coming from. After his daughter had hung up her stockings and gone to bed, he crept out into the road, round a corner out of sight, and watched. In the middle of the night, Nicholas walked down the road. He took a bag of gold coins from the pocket of his cloak, threw it into the open window so that it landed in the girl's stocking, then hurried on his way.

In Holland, parents say that Saint Nicholas brings presents every year. He comes on the night before Saint Nicholas Day, 6 December. He has a long beard, and is dressed as a bishop, with a red cloak and a pointed hat. He rides into town in the darkness of night, on a white horse whose hooves make no sound. If children have filled a shoe, or a clog, with hay and carrots for the horse, and if they've gone to sleep and don't peep, Saint Nicholas thanks them for the carrots and hay by leaving presents. In this story, the Dutch words for Saint Nicholas are Sinter Klaas – and that's how we get our words 'Santa Claus'.

Santa Claus has other names as well. Long ago, in Lapland, children believed that the sky-god, Odin, rode through the clouds on a sledge at the end of each year, punishing wicked people and giving presents to good people. His chariot was pulled by a magic, eight-legged horse called Sleepneer, or by a team of flying reindeer. When the Laplanders became Christian, they renamed Odin Father Christmas. In the story he has a bushy white beard and keeps the cold out with a thick red cloak and a fur-trimmed hood. Even in Australia, New Zealand and other countries in the Southern Hemisphere, where Christmas happens in mid-summer, people still imagine Father Christmas in a reindeer-sledge and wearing a thick red cloak and hood.

There are still more names. In Switzerland and Sweden, instead of Father Christmas, Mother Christmas comes. Her name is Lucia, which means 'Light', and she is named after Saint Lucia. Saint Lucia lived in Roman times, when Christians were often arrested and tortured. Many people hid in caves and underground tunnels – and Lucia used to take them food. She needed both hands free to carry the food, so she carried light on her head: a crown of candles. In Sweden, on 13 December (Saint Lucia's day), the eldest girl in each family puts on a long, white dress with a red sash, and a crown of silver paper to look like candles. (Real candle-crowns, which are too dangerous to wear, are hung from the ceiling. Some people call them 'Advent crowns'). The girl leads everyone in procession through the house, carrying presents of biscuits and sweets and singing a special song.

Saint Lucia, Father Christmas, Odin, Saint Nicholas – there are plenty of stories to choose from. We have taken bits from each of them, put them all together and made up the Santa Claus story we know today: the one about an old man with a beard, red cloak, hood and reindeer who slips down the chimney and leaves presents in stockings hung up by the fireplace or pinned to the end of your bed. *That* Santa Claus has never really existed. He's made up. But some of the others were real – and so are the people who leave your presents. If *they* want to go on believing in Santa Claus, don't stop them. Don't breathe a word.

Kenneth McLeish

# Christmas Day

*This extract is set in the 1890s on a farm in Derbyshire where Susan Garland lived. Susan Garland is really the author, Alison Uttley, and this is a description of how she remembered Christmas morning to be all that time ago.*

Susan awoke in the dark of Christmas morning. A weight lay on her feet, and she moved her toes up and down. She sat up and rubbed her eyes. It was Christmas Day. She stretched out her hands and found the knobby little stocking, which she brought into bed with her and clasped tightly in her arms as she fell asleep again.

She awoke later and lay holding her happiness, enjoying the moment. The light was dim, but the heavy mass of the chest of drawers stood out against the pale walls, all blue like the snowy shadows outside. She drew her curtains and looked out at the starry sky. She listened for the bells of the sleigh, but no sound came through the stillness except for the screech owl's call.

Again she hadn't caught Santa Claus. Of course she knew he wasn't real, but she also knew he was. It was the same with everything. People said things were not alive but you knew in your heart they were: statues which would catch you if you turned your back were made of stone; Santa Claus was your own father and mother; the stuffed fox died long ago.

But suppose people didn't *know*! They hadn't seen that stone woman walk in Broomy Vale Arboretum, but she might, in the dark night. They hadn't seen Santa Claus and his sleigh, but that was because they were not quick enough. Susan had nearly caught things happening to herself, she knew they only waited for her to go away. When she looked through a window into an empty room, there was always a guilty look about it, a stir of surprise.

Perhaps Santa Claus had left the marks of his reindeer and the wheels of his sleigh on the snow at the front of the house. She had never looked because last year there was no snow, and the year before she had believed in him absolutely. She would go out before breakfast, and perhaps she would find two marks of runners and a crowd of little hoof-marks.

She pinched the stocking from the toe to the top, where her white suspender tapes were stitched. It was full of nice knobs and lumps, and a flat thing like a book stuck out of the top. She drew it out – it *was* a book, just what she wanted most.

She sniffed at it, and liked the smell of the cardboard back with deep letters cut in it. She ran her fingers along like a blind man and could not read the title, but there were three words in it.

Next came an apple, with its sweet, sharp odour. She recognized it, a yellow one, from the apple chamber, and from her favourite tree. She took a bite with her strong, white little teeth and scrunched it in the dark.

It was delicious fun, all alone, in this box-like room, with the dim blue-and-white jug on the washstand watching her, and the pool of the round mirror hanging on the wall, reflecting the blue dark outside, and the texts. 'Thou God seest Me,' and 'Blessed are the Peacemakers', and 'Though your sins be as scarlet they shall be as white as wool'. They could all see the things although she couldn't, and they were glad.

Next came a curious thing, pointed and spiked, with battlements like a tower. Whatever could it be? It was smooth like ivory and shone even in the dark. She ran her fingers round the little rim and found a knob. She gave it a tug, and a ribbon flew out – it was a tape-measure to measure a thousand things, the trees' girths, the calf's nose, the pony's tail. She put it on her knee and continued her search.

There was a tin ball that unscrewed and was filled with comfits, and an orange, and a sugar mouse, all these were easy to feel, a sugar watch with a paper face and a chain of coloured ribbon, a doll's chair, and a penny china doll with a round smooth head. She at once named it Diana, after Diana of the Ephesians, for this one could never be an idol, being made of pot. She put her next to her skin down the neck of her nightdress, and pulled the last little bumps out of the stocking toe. They were walnuts, smelling of the orchards at Bird-in-Bush Farm, where they grew on great trees overhanging the wall, and a silver shilling, the only one she ever got, and very great wealth, but it was intended for the money-box in the hall. It was the nicest Christmas stocking she had ever had, and she hugged her knees up to her chin and rocked with joy. Then she put her hand under her pillow and brought out five parcels which had made five separate lumps under her head. They were quite safe.

She heard the alarm go off in her father's room and Dan's bell go jingle-jangle. Five o'clock, plenty of time yet before the hoof-marks would disappear. The wind swished softly against the window, and thumps and thuds sounded on the stairs. She slept again with the doll on her heart and the tape-measure under her cheek and the book in her hand.

She was awakened again by the rattle of milk-cans below her window. Joshua and Becky were coming back with the milk, and it really was Christmas Day. All else was strangely silent, for the deep snow deadened the sound of footsteps. She jumped out of bed, pressed her nose against the window, and rubbed away the Jack Frost pictures. Everything was blue, and a bright star shone. From a window in the farm buildings a warm gleam fell on the snow. Dan was milking the last cow by the light of the lantern which hung on the wall.

Then she heard his cheerful whistle and the low moo of the cows as he came out with the can.

What had the cattle done all night? Did they know it was Christmas? Of course, all God's creatures knew. Becky said the cows and horses knelt down on Christmas Eve. She could see them going down on their front knees, the cows so easily, the horses so painfully, for their legs were wrong. Sheep knelt when they had foot-rot, it would be easy for them. But down they all went, bowing to the New Saviour as she bowed to the new moon.

She washed in the basin with blue daisies round the rim, but she could see neither water nor soap. Candles were for night, not morning use. She brushed her hair in front of the ghost of a mirror, where a white little face looked like a flower-in-the-night. She slipped the round comb through her hair and put on her Sunday honey-combed dress with seven tucks in the skirt and two in the sleeves, a preparation for a long and lanky Susan.

Then she buttoned her slippers and said her short morning prayer, and down she tripped with her stocking-load of presents and the five parcels. She walked boldly past the fox and went to the landing window that overlooked the grass plots and lawn. The beeches were still, the apple trees stood blue and cream against the white hills, and there was a thin moon like a cow's horn in the trees.

She went into the hall and turned away from the closed kitchen door, where all was bustle, the noise of milk-cans, the roar of the fire, and the chatter of voices. The front door was unlocked and she lifted the heavy iron catch and slipped out into the virgin snow, blue and strange in the early light.

She lifted her feet high and walked to the gate in the wall surrounding the house. The monkey tree held out its arms to her, and she waved a hand. She crossed the walk and looked over the low stone wall at the lawn. There was no doubt something had been there in the night, footprints, but not hoof-marks, a fox, maybe, or a dog visiting Roger.

She returned to the house, shivering with delight, and opened the kitchen door. She was wrapped in colour and light, in sweet smells of cows and hay and coldness, brought in by the men, and new milk and hot sausages, tea and toast, warmth and burning wood from the hearth. The strongest smell was cold, which rushed through the back door sweeping all the other smells away, until the doors banged and the flame of the fire shot out.

'A merry Christmas, a merry Christmas,' she called.

Alison Uttley

# Christmas in the 1930s

When I was young Christmas Day was always spent at the houses of my Grandfather Cotton and my Grandfather Mandy. Therefore, on Christmas morning we would catch the Metropolitan Line train from North Harrow to Euston Square. It was invariably not the train intended as my mother was never ready in time for the one we planned to catch. When at last we were on the train, the relief to be sitting quietly in the warmth of the carriage after the rush and the nip of the sharp air on the open platform, where our breath had formed mini-clouds, was immense. The compartments with their twin rows of facing seats, the woodwork, the oval-framed sepia photographs of Colwyn Bay (they all seemed to be of Colwyn Bay!) and the leather-stropped windows added to the cosiness. However, for the short-trousered the moquette of the seats could be a prickly trial, leaving my legs indented with pimples like a nutmeg grater.

At Euston we caught the tram for Stamford Hill. Its rattling, clattering progress was punctuated by the ring of the conductor's ticket-punching machine which he wore firmly strapped to his chest like a warrior's breastplate. The ticket he handed you was a small oblong of thick, rough paper on which in the smallest of type were printed the names of all the stops along the tram's journey. The landmarks I remember were: the forbidding battlements of Holloway Prison (which for many years I thought was a castle), the two huge black cats sitting like sentries or Egyptian Gods at the entrance of the Carrera's Cigarette Building, and the Nag's Head public house which seemed attractively palatial and inviting.

Then, at last, Stamford Hill. We would pause to buy flowers from the great baskets, like small bright gardens, of the kerbside flower sellers, before embarking on the short walk through Christmas-Day deserted and hushed streets to Grandfather Cotton's house in the crescent. There, through the haze and incense of pipe smoke, I could make out a throng of uncles and aunts, cousins and others, crowded into a room already filled by glass cases of stuffed and exotically plumed birds. (One of my Grandfather's uncles had seen service in India and brought the collection home – or that was the story! Certainly they took up a great deal of room and were strangely out of place in that house in N15!)

'This is Auntie Beattie – you know Auntie Beattie, don't you?' It was best to nod and let them think so. She looked nice and round and kindly whoever's aunt she was and, with a bit of luck, she wouldn't kiss me. But there were so many of them! As the room filled I found myself more and more hemmed in by the peculiarly childhood forest of trouser legs, skirt hems and stocking seams. And, as each new group of the family arrived, the whole party seemed to begin all over again.

The only time voices fell quiet was when King George V's Christmas Day broadcast came on the 'wireless'. Then, when everyone was reassured that all was right with the Empire, the party renewed itself. Aunts would be giggly by this time and uncles, emboldened, decided we should have some entertainment. This was the bit I dreaded. I didn't mind Grandfather pretending to be George Robey, the great comedian of the day. No, it was the Butler brothers' efforts that I dreaded. They had a concert party in which they were pierrots (which was, I thought, the name of people who performed on the end of a pier). They dressed up in baggy costumes of white satin with great ruffs and buttons like large snowballs, and wore conical hats. Sometimes they blackened their faces to sing songs like 'Rose of England', which seemed, even at my age, to be pretty odd! But at Christmas they performed in their best suits with watch-chain decorated waistcoats and stiff, white, wing-collars. They were the only people I knew who wore these collars all the time. My dad did when he was playing the piano on special occasions, but not everyday. The Butler brothers did, however, even when such collars must have disappeared from the shops years before. Did they have a secret supply?

No costumes then, though they had come prepared. That was where my dread came in. Their special piece was their concertina band. The Butler brothers were reputed experts at playing this hexagonally-ended caterpillar. I have been told that it is a very gentle instrument. But not when a collection of them are played together in the sitting room of a house, and in the hands of players used to taking the roof off the local picture palace or competing with a force eight gale at the end of a pier. The volume was enormous. They went on and on these bespectacled brothers, like a group of musical owls. When you saw them with their concertinas fully extended, ready for a crescendo, you knew the worst was to come! I would offer a silent prayer (the only kind likely to be heard) that I would survive it all!

At length my father would pull his watch dramatically out of his pocket. 'My goodness, is it dark already?' (It had been dark for over an hour!)

'Give my regards to Mr Mandy,' Grandfather Cotton would say as he gave me the predictable Christmas present of a half-crown. Grandfather Cotton and my other grandfather, Grandfather Mandy, had known each other for over fifty years, but they still addressed each other as Mister. And always when out of working clothes they wore the formality of dark suits and white collars. Life was hard and wages low, but dignity was to be preserved.

My family would then weave its way the few hundred yards to Sherboro' Road and Grandfather Mandy's house, where Christmas dinner was waiting.

At Sherboro' Road the gas lights were lit and most of the family already assembled, for we were always the last to arrive. There was great steamy energy, bustling and activity in the haze of the scullery where the gas stove was installed and in which a regimental sized turkey was being cooked. The puddings, wrapped in white cloths, boiled noisily in the copper usually employed for the week's washing.

The table was laid in the kitchen. A large room, it could accommodate easily the sixteen or more for dinner. It was designated the kitchen because that is what it had been. Cooking, however, apart from tea-making, had long since been banished to the cavernous scullery. There was also a large built-in dresser in the kitchen with numerous drawers which when opened released a woody smell and revealed a jumble of treasures – brightly coloured threads, buttons, old photographs, ribbons, letters, postcards, playing cards, hooks and eyes, knitting needles.... There was no end to it and its promises of splendid explorations on rainy afternoons.

So there it was: the white table cloth in the gas-light, the knives, forks, spoons and plates shining in their places, the curtains drawn against the darkness outside, the coals glowing red in the fireplace, and Christmas dinner began. This meant that we would eat tea about nine o'clock at night with supper well after midnight. To be up after midnight was one of the childhood wickednesses I cherished! I still do!

For dinner there was turkey, its stuffing flavoured with a fanfare of herbs, crisp brown roasted potatoes and brussel sprouts which must have been very special. Every Brussels sprout I have eaten since has tasted as if it had begun to rot on the stalk long before picking. These were fresh and crisp. Did Grandmother have a special magic? Grandmother, a small, slightly stooping lady who, from the wax-based picture in the front room had been a beautiful dark-haired young woman, did not say much, but was comfortable to be with and a superb cook. So it would distress her to know that what I enjoyed most about our Christmas visits was the fresh bread, cold ham and pickled onions for supper! Perhaps it had more to do with the special magic of eating after midnight.

But that was later. Meanwhile we wolfed through dinner – after all we had waited long enough for it – stuffing ourselves amid banter and laughter until we reached the dark, rich, mahogony cannon ball of the Christmas pudding. My grandfather ceremoniously poured the brandy and applied a match. The resulting blue flame shot up with a whoosh and threatened the ceiling and the paper-chains that hung from it. The ceiling was too high for there to have been any real danger, but we liked to pretend there was. So the flames were greeted with shrieks and ooohs as we all feigned at being 'frightened'! We ate that sweet, fruity, substantially overnourishing confection with custard and care. Care so as not to crack a tooth or even swallow the small silver threepenny bits that were hidden in it. It was part of the ritual that Grandfather – to gasps of annual surprise – always found a half-crown in his slice. A piece of simple conjuring in which he delighted. So did we.

Then came the giving of presents. For the young, conjuring sets with

nail-through-the-finger illusions and pick-a-card tricks; dolls in chintzy dresses, with invariably blue eyes and extravagant eye lashes you could have dusted a shelf with; games of Snakes and Ladders and Happy Families with that lovable Miss Bun who seemed to be the only one who was actually happy! What secret was she cherishing, I wondered? Then there were the more practical or 'sensible' presents: endless handkerchiefs for addicted nose-blowers, and socks or loose fitting jerseys on which aunts had practised knitting. For the adults a cascade of bath-cubes, scent, ties, scarves and Christmas-wrapped sweeties.

Present-giving was followed by a frenzy of washing up in the scullery and then the great quiet. A time when the women drank tea in the kitchen or went upstairs for 'a lie down', and the men floundered like beached whales in the armchairs in the darkened front room and lit unaccustomed cigars which were to remain half smoked. A time of small movements and grampus-type breathing. A time to restore energies for the festivities to come. A time spent sleepily and slowly until, as if a switch had been thrown, the house suddenly became alive again.

It was tea-time. It was also some time *after* nine o'clock in the evening. But who cared about that? Mince pies, tarts of various jams looking like multi-coloured sunflowers, custards and curds, prissy fairy cakes, conical coconut and cherry-topped madeleines, paper-bottomed macaroons and curranty eccles cakes were relished rapidly in order to reach the Christmas cake. The Christmas cake was like the Christmas pudding in its fruity extravagance, but topped thickly with marzipan and encrusted in an armour plating of white icing which took much hacking and sawing to reduce the cake to person-sized pieces. Most of us used to leave the icing uneaten as you would the shell

of a nut or the tin from canned fruit. I suppose the icing was made that hard in order to preserve the cake inside (which it nearly did from the eaters) or, maybe, to provide work for dentists. I never discovered which. All I did know was that a slice of that cake would have sustained a person on a journey to the North Pole!

After tea, the entertainments began. It was then that uncles regretted the purchase of the conjuring set, and we regretted having learned that poem about Robin Hood in the dell and that a cousin had taken dancing lessons! Was it all a sort of punishment for having over-eaten? The games too were a bit of a trial. They were either crudely horrific, as when you were blindfolded and your finger was thrust into an orange having been told it was Nelson's eye, or they were complicated and difficult like 'Pit', a card game based on the American Wheat market, and way outside our everyday experience! It was a game forced on us by Aunt Win, the bright, modern one of the family who read books and played badminton (and whose badminton knickers were so brief Grandmother would not have them hanging on the family washing line in case the neighbours should see them). It was not until Boxing Day that card games as uncomplicated as Sevens of Brag were allowed, though as the drink eased the adults along, the rules of 'Pit' began to matter less and less and perhaps they too began to share my mistaken idea that it was a game about zoos. And so we moved on to the climaxes of the day.

First, there were the indoor fireworks, one of which produced an ashy snake and shrieks from Aunt Edna, another which filled the room with a 'snow storm' which repeated itself for days afterwards when somebody drew the curtains. Then came the singing round the piano on which my father played from the sheet music stored in the piano stool: 'Smoke gets in your eyes', 'Lady of Spain I adore you', and 'If you were the only girl in the world'. All this was followed by supper. Sweet ham accompanied by the sharpness of pickled onions, the jet secrets of pickled walnuts, the crisp, clean crunch of celery and the cheerful red of tomatoes were the last treats of the day.

The final mystery was the sleeping arrangements. My grandparents ascended to their own room on the mid-landing. The women claimed the large bedroom at the front of the house which, as aunts and mums slipped back in years, took on the hushed, whispery, giggly, atmosphere of a girls' dormitory. I and an uncle or two slept in the small bedroom at the back of the house, and the rest of the men stayed downstairs on mattresses laid out in the front room where it looked much like the drawings Henry Moore was to make in the war of people sleeping on the platforms of the London Underground. It took on the rough and ready atmosphere of a barrack room. It was all a bit prophetic if we had known, because it was the War that was to disperse the family and bring to an end these Christmas gatherings. It was the War that saw the end of the house in Sherboro' Road as well, when it was demolished by a bomb in an air raid.

The sliver of first light was just appearing when eventually we all got to sleep. The frost had already etched patterns on the windows and honed the air outside. I dreamed of the goodies to come: Boxing Day was special too.

John Cotton

# The Christmas pony

What interested me in our new neighbourhood was not the school, nor the room I was to have in the new house all to myself, but the stable which was built at the back of the house. My father let me direct the making of a stall, a little smaller than the other stalls, for my pony, and I prayed and hoped and my sister Lou believed, that that meant I would get the pony, perhaps for Christmas. I pointed out to her that there were three other stalls and no horses at all. This I said in order that she should answer it. She could not. My father, sounded out, said that some day we might have horses and a cow; meanwhile a stable added to the value of the house. 'Some day' is a pain to a boy who lives in and knows only 'now'. My good little sisters, to comfort me, remarked that Christmas was coming, but Christmas was always coming and grown-ups were always talking about it, asking you what you wanted and then giving you what they wanted you to have.

Though everybody knew what I wanted, I told them all again. My mother knew that I told God, too, every night. I wanted a pony, and to make sure they understood, I declared that I wanted nothing else.

'Nothing but a pony?' my father asked.

'Nothing,' I said.

'Not even a pair of boots?'

That was hard. I did want boots, but I stuck to the pony.

'No, not even boots.'

'Nor candy? There ought to be something to fill your stocking with, and Santa Claus can't put a pony into a stocking.

That was true, and he couldn't lead a pony down the chimney either. But no. 'All I want is a pony,' I said. 'If I can't have a pony give me nothing, nothing.'

Now I had been looking myself for the pony I wanted, going to sales stables, enquiring of horsemen, and I had seen several that would do. My father let me 'try' them. I tried so many ponies that I was learning fast to sit a horse. I chose several, but my father always found some fault with them. I was in despair. When Christmas was at hand I had given up all hope of a pony, and on Christmas Eve I hung up my stocking along with my sisters', of whom, by the way, I had three.

I haven't mentioned my sisters because, you understand, they were girls, and girls, young girls, counted for nothing in my manly life. They did not mind me either; they were so happy that Christmas Eve, that I caught some of their merriment. I speculated on what I'd get. I hung up the biggest stocking I had, and we all went reluctantly to bed to wait until morning. Not to sleep; not right away. We were told that not only must we sleep promptly, we must not wake up until seven-thirty – if we did, we must not go to the fireplace for our Christmas. Impossible.

We did sleep that night, but we woke up at six a.m. We lay in our beds and debated through the open doors whether to obey until, say, half-past six. Then we bolted. I don't know who started it, but there was a rush. We all disobeyed; we raced to disobey and get first to the fireplace in the front room downstairs. And there they were, the gifts, all sorts of wonderful things, mixed-up piles of presents; only, as I disentangled the mess, I saw that my stocking was empty; it hung limp; not a thing in it; and under and around it – nothing. My sisters had knelt down, each by her pile of gifts; they were squealing with delight, until they looked up and saw me standing there in my nightgown with nothing. They left their piles to come to me and look with me at my empty place. Nothing. They felt my stocking: nothing.

I don't remember whether I cried at that moment, but my sisters did. They ran with me back to my bed, and there we all cried until I became indignant. That helped some. I got up, dressed, and driving my sisters away, I went alone out into the yard, down to the stable, and there, all by myself, I wept. My mother came out to me by and by; she found me in my pony stall, sobbing on the floor, and she tried to comfort me. But I heard my father outside; he had come part way with her, and she was having some sort of angry quarrel with him. She tried to comfort me; besought me to come to breakfast. I could not; I wanted no comfort and no breakfast. She left me and went on into the house with sharp words for my father.

I don't know what kind of breakfast the family had. My sisters said it was 'awful'. They were ashamed to enjoy their own toys. They came to me, and I was rude. I ran away from them. I went around to the front of the house, sat down on the steps, and, the crying over, I ached. I was wronged, I was hurt – I can feel now what I felt then, and I am sure that if one could see the wounds upon our hearts, there would be found still upon mine a scar from that terrible Christmas morning. And my father, the practical joker, he must have been hurt, too, a little. I saw him looking out of the window. He was watching me or something for an hour or two, drawing back the curtain ever so little lest I should catch him, but I saw his face, and I think I can see now the anxiety upon it, the worried impatience.

After, I don't know how long, surely an hour or two, I was brought to the climax of my agony by the sight of a man riding a pony down the street, a pony and a brand new saddle; the most beautiful saddle I ever saw, and it was a boy's saddle; the mans feet were not in the stirrups; his legs were too long. The outfit was perfect; it was the realisation of all my dreams, the answer to all my prayers. A fine new bridle, with a light curb bit. And the pony! As he drew near, I saw that the pony was really a small horse – what we called an Indian pony, a bay, with black mane and tail, and one white foot and a white star on his forehead. For such a horse as that I would have given, I could have given, anything.

But the man, a dishevelled fellow with a blackened eye and a fresh-cut face, came along, reading the numbers on the houses, and, as my hopes – my impossible hopes – rose, he looked at our door and passed by, he and the pony, and the saddle and the bridle. Too much. I fell upon the steps, and having wept before, I broke now into such a flood of tears that I was a floating wreck when I heard a voice.

'Say, kid,' it said, 'do you know a boy named Lennie Steffens?'

I looked up. It was the man on the pony, back again, at our horse block.

'Yes,' I spluttered through my tears, 'That's me.'

'Well,' he said, 'then this is your horse. I've been looking all over for you and your house. Why don't you put your number where it can be seen?

'Get down,' I said running out to him.

He went on saying something about 'ought to have got here at seven o'clock; told me to bring the nag here and tie him to your post and leave him for you. But I got into a drunk – and a fight – and a hospital – and –'

'Get down,' I said.

He got down, and he boosted me up to the saddle. He offered to fit the stirrups for me, but I didn't want him to. I wanted to ride.

'What's the matter with you? he said, angrily. 'What you crying for? Don't you like the horse? He's a dandy, this horse. I know him of old. He's fine at cattle; he'll drive 'em alone.'

I hardly heard, I could scarcely wait, but he persisted. He adjusted the stirrups, and then, finally, off I rode, slowly, at a walk, so happy, so thrilled,

that I did not know what I was doing. I did not look back at the house or the man, I rode off up the street, taking note of everything – of the reins, of the pony's long mane, of the carved leather saddle. I had never known anything so beautiful. And mine! I was going to ride up past Miss Kay's house. But I noticed on the horn of the saddle some stains like rain-drops, so I turned and trotted home, not to the house but to the stable. There was the family, father, mother, sisters, all working for me, all happy. They had been putting in place the tools of my new business: blankets, curry-comb, brush, pitchfork – everything, and there was hay in the loft.

'What did you come back so soon for?' somebody asked. 'Why didn't you go on riding?'

I pointed to the stains. 'I wasn't going to get my new saddle rained on,' I said. And my father laughed. 'It isn't raining,' he said. 'Those are not rain-drops.'

'They are tears,' my mother gasped, and she gave my father a look which sent him off to the house. Worse still, my mother offered to wipe away the tears still running out of my eyes. I gave her such a look as she had given him, and she went off after my father, drying her own tears. My sisters remained and we unsaddled the pony, put on his halter, led him to his stall, tied and fed him. It began really to rain; so all the rest of that memorable day we curried and combed that pony. The girls plaited his mane, forelock, and tail, while I pitchforked hay to him and curried and brushed, curried and brushed. For a change we brought him out to drink; we led him up and down, blanketed like a race-horse; we took turns at that. But the best, the most inexhaustible fun, was to clean him. When we went reluctantly to our midday Christmas dinner, we all smelt of horse, and my sisters had to wash their faces and hands. I was asked to, but I wouldn't until my mother bade me look in the mirror. Then I washed up – quick. My face was caked with the muddy lines of tears that had coursed over my cheeks to my mouth. Having washed away that shame, I ate my dinner, and as I ate I grew hungrier and hungrier. It was my first meal that day, and as I filled up on the turkey and the stuffing, the cranberries and the pies, the fruit and the nuts – as I swelled, I could laugh. My mother said I still choked and sobbed now and then, but I laughed, too; I saw and enjoyed my sisters' presents until – I had to go out and attend to my pony, who was there, really and truly there, the promise, the beginning of a happy double life. And – I went and looked to make sure – there was the saddle, too, and the bridle.

But that Christmas, which my father had planned so carefully, was it the best or the worst I ever knew? He often asked me that; I never could answer as a boy. I think now that it was both. It covered the whole distance from broken-hearted misery to bursting happiness – too fast. A grown-up could hardly have stood it.

Lincoln Steffens

# Seven shopping days to Christmas

Grimble's parents were very forgetful. This was sometimes annoying, but having a forgetful father and mother also had advantages. For instance it meant that he had better bedtimes than most other children. Quite often he used to go into his father's room and say, 'I'm going to bed now; it's midnight', and his father would say, 'Don't wait up for me' or, 'Iquique is the only town I know with two qs!'

For most of the year Grimble – Grimble was his whole name, his parents had forgotten to give him any other names – rather enjoyed having a father and mother who were different from those of the other boys at school, but when it came to Christmas there were very definite disadvantages.

Grimble had only two more days of school before the Christmas holidays started – and the old Grimbles went around as if it were the middle of February or the end of August; anyway, there was nothing special about the way they went around. The shops in the High Street had windows decorated with lights and Father Christmases and wrapped-up packages and mince pies and a big notice saying ONLY SEVEN MORE SHOPPING DAYS TO CHRISTMAS on which the number of days before the twenty-fifth was changed every evening... it was very exciting.



And Grimble's mother went out with a big shopping bag – and came back with a cabbage, and one and a half pounds of cod fillets. I don't want to be unkind about cod fillets. They are perfectly all right, but they just do not make you tingle all over. Anyway, they didn't make Grimble tingle all over.

Grimble had a friend called David Sebastian Waghorn whose mother had said, 'We are going to have cold turkey on Boxing Day.' That is just about the same as saying, 'On Christmas Day, we are going to have hot roast turkey with stuffing and gravy and sausages and bacon and roast potatoes and Brussels sprouts.' He waited anxiously for Mrs Grimble to give some small hint like that. The evening before she had said, 'Have you put the cat out?' and Grimble said, 'We haven't got a cat,' and Mrs Grimble said, 'Oh dear, nor we have, don't forget to leave her a saucer of milk.'

Grimble watched his parents carefully for any sign that they might have remembered why he was going to be on holiday and when, and what sort of treats he was going to get if he was going to get treats. He worked hard giving them well-mannered hints because it was terribly important to him that Christmas would be, well... complete.

One evening he dropped a lot of pine needles on the carpet... but as no one noticed or said anything and Grimble was very tidy, he got a dust-pan and brush and swept them up again a couple of days later.

Also he tried to hum Good King Wenceslaus... mm mmmmmmmm mm mmmmmm m but he did not hum very well and his father thinking it was God Save The Queen, stood up and when Grimble had finished humming his father turned off the television set and went to bed.

So he practised humming some more. David Sebastian Waghorn had a joke about humming. 'Do you know why humming birds hum? Because they don't know the words.' Grimble thought David Sebastian Waghorn was a very funny boy.

The day before, Mr Grimble had come into the house with a large square parcel and Grimble, knowing that it was not polite to be openly curious, had gone into the kitchen and watched his father take the parcel into the study through the slightly open door. It looked as if it might be a bicycle taken to pieces or a large box kite or possibly a new kind of cooker.

That evening his father said, 'Come into the study and see what I've got in my parcel. It's a foot-stool, I gave it to me...' and Grimble had clenched his teeth and said, 'Now you can lie back in your chair and you don't even have to bend your legs.' His father was delighted that Grimble had got the point of the footstool so quickly and showed him where Iquique was on the globe of the world... it was about half-way down South America on the left-hand side.

'Do you expect to get anything else for Christmas... except for my presents...' he asked his father in an off hand way. 'A lot of weather,' said his father who had just found Birmingham on the globe.

That night when Grimble was in bed he started to think about Christmas very seriously. Christmas was a holiday and a time for eating interesting food and giving presents and receiving presents – someone had told him that it was more blessed to do one than the other, but he kept forgetting which. Now the reason why children expected their parents to do things for them at Christmas was because parents are better organised than children and parents have more money than children.

In Grimble's case this was only partly true. His parents were not nearly as well organised as he; they kept forgetting to get up in the morning and sometimes forgot to go to bed for days on end and they never knew what time it was.

But the old Grimbles did have more money than he... or he hoped they did, because Grimble only had £1.90 and an Irish 5p piece. He lay in bed practising his humming and wondering whether, if one was really well organised, as he was – satchel packed; homework done; toothpaste squeezed out on to toothbrush; tie tied in a knot and opened out into a big loop so that it would go over his head; shoelaces done up so that he could step into his shoes and wriggle them about till the heels gave way... anyway, if someone were really well organised, it should not be very difficult for him to make money... and if he had money then he could arrange the whole family Christmas celebrations.

One evening Grimble had listened

to a television programme about money in which a man had said the important thing was to find something that everyone needed. That way, you had a ready market for whatever you were going to sell... for instance, the man explained: 'It is a better thing to go from house to house selling socks, which everyone wears, than suspenders – which are rubber straps that go round your leg below the knee and keep the socks up. Hardly anyone wears suspenders,' said the man. Grimble had never even heard of suspenders. 'Also,' said the man, 'you have to spend some of your money on getting people interested in your wares – this is called advertising.'

Grimble was very impressed and wrote a small note to remind himself: to sell successfully you have to find something everyone wants, and advertise it.

It was quite clear to Grimble that if a man wants to earn money by selling things, he would have to buy them first; the simple problem that Grimble had was what could he buy for £1.90 that he might be able to sell for a lot of money – because a turkey and a Christmas pudding and presents and everything would cost pounds. One of the teachers at school had told them about an old Greek who was lying in a bathtub when an apple fell on his head and he shouted, 'Eureka, I've got it!' and invented gold, or something like that. Grimble lay in his bed thinking waiting to shout, 'Eureka, I've got it!' but he fell asleep.

In the morning he went to the shop on the corner and as it was empty he looked carefully around for something that everyone needed that cost £1.90 or less. There were rolls of flypaper and some suntan cream and washing soap and tins of sardines and lemonade crystals. These were all dusty, which is a bad sign. Suddenly he saw a loaf of bread and a great idea occurred to him: everyone needed bread; if he went around selling bread slice by slice to people so that they didn't have to go to shops he could become very rich. And then he thought most people already have bread, but if I sold toast... not only sold it but took it to people just when they wanted it. When they were sitting at the breakfast table with butter on the knife and a marmalade jar in front of them... the GRIMBLE HOME TOAST DELIVERY SERVICE. Proprietor Grimble. 'Eureka I've got it!' he shouted and the old lady came out from the back of the shop and said, 'If you've got it you'd better pay for it. That is the only way you can do things in a shop.'

Grimble was much too excited to explain, so he paid the lady 60p which was the price of that loaf of bread and went to school.

He didn't learn much at school that day because he was working out his toast business. The loaf of bread was in his locker; it was a cut loaf called THIN SLICED which seemed a silly name to give a loaf and it contained eighteen pieces of bread in a plastic bag. (If the business really succeeds he thought, I might go into the plastic bag business.)

Every morning nearly everyone eats toast and, as toast is quite boring to make, Grimble decided that if he made toast at seven every morning and brought it to people all hot and ready they would definitely pay 25p for three slices, which meant six times three slices in a loaf which is £1.50 back for 60p.

When he came home from school he sat down at his desk and got a large piece of paper and cut it in half and then cut each half in half again and then halved the four pieces of paper so that he had eight small pieces and on each one he wrote the message THE GRIMBLE HOME TOAST DELIVERY SERVICE PROPRIETOR GRIMBLE founded 1992. On the other side he wrote: Toast delivered, daily, tidily, unburntly, punctually. 25p for three slices. Our representative will call tomorrow morning with a free slice and awaits the pleasure of your order.

He took the eight pieces of paper and put four of them through the letter boxes of the four houses up the hill from his house and posted the other four through the doors on the downhill side. As he was going back home he decided that as he did not know a great deal about toast he had better go and see Madame Beryl, who was a fat kind friend of his mother's who kept a bakery shop and knew a lot about things like that.

'Good afternoon,' said Grimble, entering the shop. 'I would like to have a small discussion with you about bread.' 'I prefer,' said Madame Beryl, 'to talk about cake.' 'I meant to say toast,' said Grimble. 'I still meant cake,' said Madame Beryl. She eased her right foot out of her shoe, which came away with a small sigh of relief, and said, 'I would very much like to talk to you about bread AND toast but unfortunately I have to go and see a man about a wedding breakfast. Can it wait until after Christmas?'

'I am afraid,' said Grimble, 'that after Christmas will be exactly too late.' There was a small silence. 'I have done a very silly thing,' said Madame Beryl. 'I baked a cake which had not been ordered and now I don't know what to do with it and the dustbin is full. Do you think you would be very kind and take possession of it?' 'Oh, yes, thank you,' said Grimble, 'if it really is in your way.' And Madame Beryl put her foot back into her protesting shoe, got a quite large cake, gave it to Grimble, said, 'Oh dear, I must fly,' and started moving into the street like a cabin trunk. 'About toast,' said Grimble following her. 'Not toast,' puffed Madame Beryl. 'Never toast cake. Ice it with icing sugar and egg white,' and she waddled onto a bus.

Grimble found himself alone with a cake and then he thought, actually a cake with icing is a very Christmassy thing to have and tomorrow I shall start up my business and in nine days' time it will be Christmas Eve and even if my parents have forgotten, it's going to be an absolutely complete proper well organised Christmas.

Clement Freud

# Pantomimes

In most British towns and cities, theatres put on special shows at Christmas. The shows are pantomimes, and the theatres are packed with people laughing, singing, clapping and enjoying themselves.

Hundreds of years ago, if you'd gone to see a Christmas play, it would have been in a castle hall. It would have been the story of a contest between good and evil. There would have been a hero, a monster and dozens of imps and demons. The hero would have been wounded in a swordfight, then brought back to life by a magic potion and gone on to win. There would have been other things to enjoy as well as the play: singers, sword-swallowers, jugglers, dancers, acrobats and performing animals.

These entertainments usually happened just once a year, on 28 December. The three weeks before was a special topsy-turvy time. On 6 December, one choirboy from the church was chosen to be 'Boy Bishop'. For three weeks, he wore bishop's clothes, and sat in the bishop's throne. The play, and the acts which went with it, were celebrations to close his reign.

In the time of Queen Elizabeth I, rich people and courtiers also enjoyed watching Christmas entertainments. The entertainments were called masques – not because the actors wore masks, but because 'masque' is an old word for 'theatre show'. Instead of good-and-evil stories, full of sword-fights, masques used tales from myth and legend, or Bible stories. There was singing and dancing – and at the banquet after the masque, a jester performed. He wore a two-coloured costume (one side red, one yellow) and a hat like a cock's comb with bells on it. He told jokes, juggled and sang to entertain the guests. One favourite trick was to put on a skirt, apron and bonnet, run in with a rolling-pin or water-bucket and pretend to be an angry cook or washerwoman.

In the century after Elizabeth's reign, the government disapproved of dancing and acting, and banned them by law. Theatres were closed, and performers had to find other jobs. It was fifty years until the law was changed and plays could be performed again.

This is when pantomimes began. They used many of the old Christmas-play ideas, forgotten during the dark, closed years. There were new ideas as well, and gradually pantomimes grew into the kind of entertainment we know today.

A modern pantomime doesn't take its story from the Bible, or from myth or legend. It uses a fairy tale: Cinderella, Aladdin, Jack and the Beanstalk. One favourite pantomime is based on a real person – Dick

Whittington, a boy who went to London to seek his fortune and ended up Lord Mayor. In every pantomime story, the hero (or in Cinderella, the heroine) goes from rags to riches, helped by magic beings such as fairy godmothers or genies. These stories are just like the old good-and-evil plays, except that magic beings replace the demons – and are usually on the hero's side.

Everyone knows the story of a pantomime before they go to see it. We're not really surprised when Jack plants his bean and it grows into a vast stalk which carries him to a giant's castle in the clouds. No one is astonished when a genie appears in a flash of smoke from Aladdin's lamp, or when Cinderella is transformed into a princess in glass slippers (at least till midnight). We don't expect surprises in pantomime. We expect enjoyment of other kinds.

This is where the comedy comes in. If you're writing a pantomime, you cram your basic story with as many comedy characters as you can think of. The giant or the wizard needs servants? Fine, make them comedians. The hero needs neighbours, and the neighbours need jobs? Fine, make them comical house-decorators or window cleaners, or plumbers. The villain needs fiendish henchmen to work his wicked will? Fine, make them really dastardly, so that the audience will boo and hiss every time they come on stage.

Two kinds of comedy characters are particular favourites. One is the Dame. The Dame is usually played by the chief comedian, and is a man in drag (that is, playing a woman). Cinderella has two dames – the Ugly Sisters. The Dame is always getting involved in slapstick fights: rolling-pin rows, pie-throwing, water-splashing – just like the cooks or washerwomen jesters used to play at Elizabethan feasts. The Dame also does comedy dancing, and sings comic songs which the audience help along.

The second favourite comedy character is a magic animal. In Dick Whittington, it is the Cat. In Mother Gocse, it is the Goose. In Jack and the Beanstalk, it is usually a cow called Daisy. The magic animal can talk, sing, do acrobatics and above all dance. The Goose lays golden eggs. Daisy the cow flutters her eyelashes and has udders labelled 'Full Cream', 'Skimmed' and sometimes 'Tea' and 'Coffee'. These creatures are played by actors and dancers, in specially-made costumes. It takes two people to play a cow. The front person stands upright, playing the front legs and the head. The back person bends down, clutching the front person's waist, to play the body and back legs.

Once you have a story and plenty of comedy, the next ingredient is music. In the old days, most pantomimes had specially-written songs. But nowadays writers often use pop songs and other audience favourites. Well-known actors and comedians use their own songs, dances and acts, built into the pantomime story. Some people dislike this. They say that pop music and TV comedy have nothing to do with pantomime, and should be kept out of it. Others disagree. They say that the fun of pantomime is that you can put into it whatever you like. A hero played by a woman? A Dame played by a man? A conjurer? A group of high-kicking dancers? An impressionist? A sword swallower, just like the old days? No problem! A good pantomime should be like a Christmas pudding, stuffed with goodies, a delicious way to celebrate a happy, holiday time of year.

Kenneth McLeish

# Who needs Superman!

It was two days after Christmas on a dark, dingy, dismal, ding-bat of a December afternoon when my parents disappeared. Well, they had gone off to visit my aunty really, the aunty who had given me a super-duper, double-trouble, multi-coloured torch for Christmas. I bet you can guess how popular I had become, shooting everything and everyone in sight with its different coloured lights. I'd quickly learned how to spring out in a surprise attack and blast away... POW... GREEN!... POW... BLUE!... POW... RED!... POW... GOTCHA!

Now, on this particular afternoon, I had persuaded my parents that I should, very unselfishly, stay at home and look after the television. This was just in case it got lonely and wanted to talk to someone. So, as soon as my parents had zoomed off, I zoomed over and switched it on. I just wanted to check that it was feeling okay.

As I had woken up the television, I thought I may as well just flick through the various channels to check that there was nothing upsetting it. Flick... flick... flick – yes, the television seemed quite happy and colourful, as well as having plenty to say for itself. In fact, as the screen was rather interesting, and not wanting to upset it, I settled down to check out the story-line.

We were getting on really well and the television had just introduced me to Superman, when all of a sudden I heard a strange, chilling noise, RAP! RAP! My stomach did a handstand and my brain pretended not to listen. Besides I didn't want to distract Superman, who at that precise moment, was telling me all about his Krypton Powers. RAP! RAP! But there it was again, coming, I thought, from the dining-room. RAP! RAP! It was clearer this time. I shivered, then quivered, and suddenly it felt as if a huge, hairy caterpillar was doing a forward roll along my body. I swallowed and found my throat to be dry and my tongue like an extra double-strength tissue.

RAP! RAP! There it was again! This time my eyebrows jumped up and disappeared over the back of my head. 'Hairy canaries,' I grumbled and in desperation I looked at the television, wondering if Superman had heard the noise. 'Come on, superhero, get yourself round to my

house and sort out this lark in the dark,' I mumbled. But Superman was supporting a collapsing bridge at the time. So I leaned over, wished him good luck and switched him off.

'Who needs Superman?' I thought, as I crept towards the living-room door which at that moment seemed more like the dying-room door, for as I reached for the handle THAT noise threatened again.

'What was it and who could it be?' asked a frightened little voice in my head. A burglar, a murderer, a cat, a dog, a budgie, a crocodile or even a gggggghhhhoooossst – wwwhhhooo knew?

I ducked under two Christmas balloons that appeared to have shrivelled up in fear and I slipped through the doorway, thinking why couldn't I have been a door? Doors have no responsibilities, no worries and certainly *no* funny noises to deal with, just a lot of hanging around. On second thoughts, I couldn't handle it. RAP! RAP! RAP! RAP! Double the dose this time. Just like medicine, but twice as bad.

I dragged the back of my hand across my mouth and tasted the sweat that seemed to be leaking everywhere from my body.

'Come on you yellow fellow and get into that room,' I muttered to myself as my feet felt as if they were growing roots.

RAP! RAP! There it was again and *definitely* getting louder. Perhaps it was a four-eyed, goggle-eyed, green-eyed, cross-eyed, creepy-peepy monster from outer space! I blinked to stop my eyeballs getting bigger. They felt as though they were going to explode to the size of footballs. I slid towards the back of the house and the dining-room door where I searched for the handle and twisted it. The door shot open almost of its own accord. I grabbed at it, but it sailed ahead into the darkness eager to get where it was going, which was more than can be said for me.

Silence, followed by more silence. Followed by...? Perhaps that was breathing I could hear. Perhaps the four-eyed creepy-peepy was waiting to dive out on me. Perhaps I would scream 'AAAAAAAAAAGH!' as it blasted me with its laser-beam eyes. Perhaps... perhaps not. I wanted to be around for a few more Christmases.

The room was black and I wanted to paint it yellow, so I sneaked my hand up towards the light switch. Then I remembered the torch nestling in my pocket. I pulled it out slowly as though I was Arthur drawing Excalibur from the stone. Meanwhile, my lungs borrowed an extra mouthful of air. Anymore and I would have been floating across the room. I tried to swallow. I could feel a knot in my neck. I weakly whispered to myself, 'Ready, steady, – GO!'

I rolled into the room like a gunslinger and fired my torch – POW! Nothing. UUGH! I now desperately flashed the yellow light around stabbing into the darkness.

POW! POW! POW! POW!
POW! POW!
POW! POW!

Still nothing. Where was it? What was it? The only thing I knew was it had to be in the room... *somewhere*!

RAP! RAP! I gulped as the knot in my neck tightened. I couldn't swallow. Creepy-peepy had got the drop on me. Oh no, it was behind me. I spun like a turbo-charged revolving door and, expecting the worst, fired again. Suddenly the splash of torch light revealed the guilty beast. There it lay, all crumpled and alone in the corner of the room – a single piece of Christmas wrapping paper!

Ian Souter

# Images in Bethlehem

*They came to Bethlehem at dusk*
*A man, a woman on an ass*
*Gently he lifted her from its back*
*She swayed unsteady on her feet*
*and clung to him*
*For a moment they stood*
*Three figures etched against the canvas of a*
*darkening sky like silhouettes.*

I came out of the inn and saw the travellers near the well.

'Shalom!' the man greeted me. 'Good friend, will you stay with Mary my wife, while I speak with the inn-keeper?'

'Master,' I said, 'if you seek lodging you will not find any here. Even on the cold floor of the cook-house travellers spread their sleeping mats at night.'

But the man would not be put off.

'I must try for my wife's sake,' he said. 'She is weak from the journey and needs rest.'

And he hurried into the inn.

Mary's eyes were gentle and wise beyond her years. I think that she was not much older than my thirteen years. The man could have been father to her. I sat down beside her on the resting stone.

'I am Naomi and work here at the inn. Have you journeyed far?'

'Five days we have been on the road from Nazareth. After the second day of our journey, Joseph's mule was stolen and he is weary and footsore, though he tries to hide it from me.'

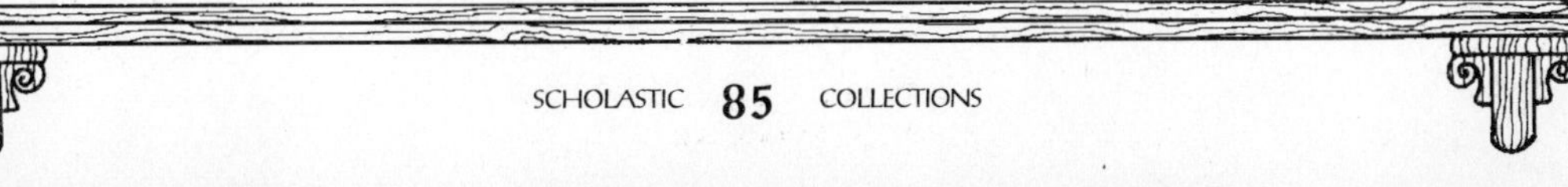

'Have you no friends in Bethlehem where you might find shelter?' I asked.
'Oh yes,' she answered, 'we shall stay with Joseph's family in the city but we need a place to rest tonight.'
We saw Joseph coming and rose to meet him.
'Mary, my beloved, we must go on to the next inn. There is no room here,' he said.
'The next inn!' I exclaimed. I looked at the three travellers. The man's eyes were red-rimmed from lack of sleep, the woman was big with child, and the donkey! Well, they would be robbed, or worse, just for that bag of bones of a donkey. They wouldn't get as far as the next village and that was closer than the next inn. I made up my mind.
'Come with me,' I said. 'I have a shelter close by. There you'll be safe and warm for the night.'
My lantern's thin beam of light pointed the way through pine forest and up a rough narrow track. On either side there were steep rock walls honeycombed with caves. My cave was the last and well-hid. Even in the light of day you could pass the entrance and not see it. The cave was dark and cold when we entered. Maybe it would seem frightening to a stranger but since my mother had died and left me an orphan, it was home to me. I knew every step of ground and patch of wall in it. I kindled a fire and soon the cave was warm and bright. The animals – a cow and its calf, a ram and two ewes – had settled down for the night but when the donkey ambled across to join them they made room for it.
'Are these your animals?' asked Joseph.
'No,' I said, 'when I found the cave they were already here. We share in peace.'
We supped well on a loaf of bread and chunks of fish baked with olives I had brought with me from the inn. Afterwards we drank fresh goat's milk and ate some dates. I offered them my bed made with pine branches and hay.

Every week I changed the hay so the bed was sweet and clean.

'Where will *you* sleep?' Mary asked.

'I will be warm enough near the animals. I often sleep with them when the nights are cold,' I said. And that was the truth.

She hugged and kissed me. Joseph put his hands on my head and said, 'Peace be with you always, Naomi. You have fed and sheltered, and even given your bed to strangers.'

He took some bedding from a bundle and laid a blanket over the branches and hay for Mary to lie on. He spread another over her to keep her warm. Then he laid himself down on his sleeping mat.

Soon there was only the sound of crackling as the fire-wood burned.

There was peace in the cave.

*The hills of Bethlehem resound*
*with rhapsodies from distant spheres*
*a paean of peace and joy*
*And hosts of angels from on high*
*swirling and whirling like dervishes*
*in a dance of ecstasy*
*worship a baby boy.*

Next morning I said to Joseph, 'Master, I can see that Mary will soon give birth. Rest here awhile for her sake.'

It was well that he agreed for on that very night the child was born. And what a night it was!

When the animals heard the baby crying they crowded around.

At once the child began to make happy sounds as though he was laughing and talking with the animals. Then they knelt down before the baby and made *their* noises. To hear them you would have thought they were trying to sing a lullaby.

In the midst of all this we heard a scuffling sound outside the cave and a man entered carrying a lamb. When he saw us he drew back and said, 'I didn't know that anyone lived here. My flock grazes on the meadows beyond the hills above. I heard the cries of animals and came to see whether any of mine had strayed.'

I welcomed him and showed him the animals kneeling around the baby.

'Glory be! What kind of child is this that animals kneel before him?' he asked in wonder.

'You come in time to celebrate our son's birth,' said Joseph. 'Will you share some mead with us?'

'Gladly,' said the shepherd, 'and offer as a gift my lamb who followed me of her own accord.'

Suddenly the animals ceased their cries.

There was a great stillness.

The fire I had lit earlier was dying but the cave flooded with a light so bright that there was not a dark place or shadow in it. As I looked around I saw that each face shone as though it was lit up from inside, and the baby was bathed in a golden glow. All the lines of pain had gone from around Mary's eyes and they were soft with love.

The shepherd broke the silence.

'Strange! I come here weary and cold from tramping the hills. Now, I want to run and leap and shout for joy. What has happened? I have never felt like this.'

'The mead was strong and makes us merry and light of spirit,' I said. Yet even as I said it I knew that was not the reason. And Mary smiled as though she held a secret too precious to share with us.

'What will you call your son?'

'His name is Jeshua,' said Mary.

'A name that is rightly his,' said the shepherd, 'for I believe that he is the One who will bring salvation to his people, as it has been foretold by the prophets.'

And everyone present was filled with joy that night, and marvelled.

Grace Hallworth

# PLAYS

## The smallest Christmas tree

*Make five green felt Christmas trees of varying sizes and decorate them on one side. Make five felt animals of varying sizes – for example a horse, a cow, a dog, a rabbit and a kitten.*
*Read the story and let the children 'act' out the play using the felt pieces on a felt board. At first, the trees should be placed so that the plain side is outwards. However, when each animal 'decorates' a tree, the tree can be turned over to show the decorated side and the appropriate animal can be placed beside it.*

In a forest there were five little fir trees. The first one said, 'I'm the biggest, so I'm the best. I'll be a big Christmas tree.'

The second one said, 'I'm the next biggest. I'll be a good Christmas tree.'

The third one said, 'I'm the middle-sized one. I'm not too big, and I'm not too small. I'm going to be a Christmas tree like the first two.'

The fourth one said, 'I'm not the smallest. I could be a Christmas tree, too.'

The littlest one sighed and said bravely, 'I know I'm the smallest, but you were all small once too. One day I'll be a Christmas tree.'

Along came some animals. First came the horse. He saw the biggest tree. 'Look,' he said. 'There's the biggest one. Just the right size for me.' So he decorated it. It was just beautiful. The horse whinnied and tossed his mane.

Next came the cow. 'Here's one just the right size for me.' The cow decorated the tree. 'Isn't it beautiful!' she mooed.

The dog came next. 'Well I never,' he barked cheerfully, 'here's a middle sized one, about right for me.' He took the third tree and decorated it. 'Woof, woof!' he barked. 'I like it!'

Along came a rabbit. She took the fourth tree to decorate.

Last of all came a kitten. He saw the smallest tree. 'There's one just the right size,' he mewed. Decorating it, he said, 'It's just *purr-fect* now!'

Winifred B. Cooper

# Is it true?

*Mary and Joseph are sitting by the manger. A crowd of people are standing round them trying to see the baby Jesus. The Kings are blocking the view of the Shepherds. You can use fewer shepherds than scripted if necessary and let each one speak more than one line.*

**Characters**

Mary, Joseph, Shepherds, Kings.

| | |
|---|---|
| **Shepherd 1** | I can't see the baby. |
| **Shepherd 2** | Neither can I. |
| **Shepherd 3** | Look over their heads. |
| **Shepherd 4** | Their heads are too high. |
| **Shepherd 5** | Well peep through their legs. |
| **Shepherd 6** | Their legs are too low. |
| **Shepherd 7** | We shouldn't have come. |
| **Shepherd 8** | We'll just have to go. |
| **Shepherd 9** | We've come so far. |
| **Shepherd 10** | Yes, such a long way. |
| **Shepherd 11** | We'll have to turn back. |
| **Shepherd 12** | No, I want to stay. |
| **Shepherd 13** | We've nothing to give him. |
| **Shepherd 14** | No, not a thing. |
| **Shepherd 15** | I know what we'll do. |
| **All** | What? |
| **Shepherd 15** | Just stand here and sing! |

| | |
|---|---|
| | *(All Shepherds sing 'Is it true?' – see page 133 for music.)* |
| | Baby Jesus can you hear us?<br>We have brought a song for you.<br>Baby Jesus, someone told us<br>You're our new King, is it true?<br>The starlight shines in the sky above<br>Is it true little baby, you're a King of love?<br>The starlight shines in the sky above<br>Is it true little baby, you're a King of love? |
| **Joseph** | Who is that singing?<br>*(Kings move to other side of crib. Shepherds move forward.)* |
| **All shepherds** | It is us. |
| **Mary** | Please sing again. |
| **All shepherds** | *(All shepherds repeat song.)* |
| **All kings** | Yes, it's true. |

Ann Bryant

# Five little fir trees

*This play can be performed by very young children, but if they are to do so successfully it is a good idea to be the woodcutter yourself. The play begins with the five trees standing in a row facing the audience. The children can be made to look like trees by wearing large, green capes or by holding large tree-shapes made from wood or card.*

**Characters**

Five trees, Woodcutter, children to decorate the trees, children to recite the poem.

Five little fir trees
Made their branches shake and soar.
Woodcutter chopped one down.
Then there were four.

*The trees move their hands up and down and flutter their fingers. Woodcutter touches one tree and the child bobs down and stays still.*

Four little fir trees
Waved branches like the sea.
Woodcutter chopped one down.
Then there were three.

*The trees move their hands from side to side, wiggling their fingers. Woodcutter touches one tree and the child bobs down and stays still.*

Three little fir trees
Let the gentle breezes through.
Woodcutter chopped one down.
Then there were two.

*The trees put their hands in the air and move their fingers gently. Woodcutter touches one tree and the child bobs down and stays still.*

Two little fir trees
Stood, like statues, in the sun.
Woodcutter chopped one down.
Then there was one.

*The trees stand absolutely still. Woodcutter touches one tree and the child bobs down and stays still.*

One little fir tree
Was weeping in the wood.
Woodcutter chopped it down.
Not a fir tree stood.

*Tree pretends to cry, rubs eyes gently with hand. Woodcutter touches the tree and the child bobs down and stays still.*

Five little fir trees
Bought in shops by girls and boys.
Were taken home and trimmed with
Every kind of fancy toys.

*All the trees stand up straight ready to be decorated. The children run up to the trees.*

Now five little fir trees
Make Christmas bright and gay
With starry lights a-twinkling
In a very special way.

*Woodcutter and the rest of the children hang baubles and tinsel from the trees.*

Rosalia Makinson

# The magic Christmas logs

*This play is intended for infants. It uses a very flexible cast and includes sections where suitably pitched improvisation is possible. The songs and music are given in the song section* *(see pages 140 to 143).*

**Characters**

Narrator, Johnny Greedylump, Jenny Greedylump, Jimmy Greedylump (dressed as desired), Mr Woodman (dressed in working clothes), Logs (dressed in brown), six Grumpydumps (dressed in dreary clothes), five Lazyslumps (beautifully groomed), Wood fairies (fairy costumes), Trees (dressed in browns and greens), Flames (dressed in orange, yellow and red), Percussion players.

## Scene I

*The trees should be dotted about the stage making interesting shapes. Use music to suggest a magic wood such as 'Scherzo' from* Midsummer Night's Dream *by Mendelssohn or any Georges Zamphyr panpipes track, or music of your choice. After about half a minute the music fades.*

**Narrator** Father Christmas knows exactly what to do when children don't behave themselves. They don't get any presents! But it's more of a problem when grown-ups don't behave themselves. Father Christmas, being Father Christmas, though, has come up with a very good idea. *(Wood fairies fly in and out of all the trees until the narrator finishes speaking.)* He sends his magic wood fairies all over the world two or three times a year. The fairies fly over woods and forests everywhere showering every single tree with the tiniest drop of fairy dew. Therefore when the trees are chopped up into logs and put into people's fireplaces, they'll only burn into a bright fire if the people are not greedy, not grumpy and not lazy. Let's see what happens to the Greedylumps.... *(Wood fairies fly off stage.)*

## Scene II

*Enter Greedylumps, eating food greedily and saying things like: 'Yum yum this is lovely', 'Get off, that's mine..' and so on. Improvise this section using other phrases to suggest how greedy the Greedylumps are. This should continue until the music starts for the 'Greedylumps' exercise song'* *(see page 140).* *Play through the first verse and then let the children who are on stage sing this verse while Johnny Greedylump reaches up high, then down to touch his toes, in time with the music. Play the second verse on the piano and then let the children sing while Jenny Greedylump jumps feet apart, with arms out to sides; then feet*

*together with arms by sides, in time to the music. Play through the third verse and then let the children sing it while Jimmy Greedylump runs on the spot in time to the music.*

**Johnny** I'm freezing.

**Jenny** Me too. I wish we had some logs to make a fire.

**Jimmy** I wish we had some sense.

**Johnny and Jenny** Why?

**Jimmy** Because if we had any sense we would have got some logs before we ran out!

**Jenny** *(Pointing to back of audience.)* Look, there's Mr Woodman I bet he's got some logs.

**Greedylumps** *(Call out together.)* Mr Woodman! *(Mr Woodman starts to walk down the aisle, through the audience, followed by Logs.)*

**Mr Woodman** *(As he approaches.)* What do you want?

**Johnny** Have you got any logs?

**Mr Woodman** Only the usual sort.

**Jimmy** What do you mean?

**Mr Woodman** The sort of logs that don't work if you're lazy. *(By now Mr Woodman and the Logs should be on stage with the Greedylumps.)*

**Greedylumps** *(To audience.)* We're not lazy, are we? *(Holds up 'No' sign for audience's benefit.)*

**Audience** No!

**Mr Woodman** And they don't work if you're grumpy.

**Greedylumps** *(To audience.)* We're not grumpy, are we?

**Audience** *(Responding to sign.)* No!

**Mr Woodman** And they don't work if you're GREEDY!

**Greedylumps** *(To each other.)* We're definitely not greedy, are we?

**All cast** *(Shout.)* Yes!

**Greedylumps** Oh no we're not.

**All Cast** Oh yes you are.

**Greedylumps** Oh no we're not.

**Mr Woodman** That's enough! Let's see if the logs burn. Then we'll know whether you're greedy or not.

**Greedylumps** Good idea!

**All Cast** Logger logger lie down
Lie down low.
Logger logger lie down
And make the fire go!
*(One Log lies down. Repeat this verse as each log lies down. Logs should lie close together.)*

| | |
|---|---|
| **Log 1** | Sorry. |
| **Log 2** | Can't do it. |
| **Log 3** | Can't be done. |
| **Log 4** | No can do. |
| **Log 5** | Not possible. |
| | *(If you are using more Logs or want to improvise here, make up similar lines.)* |
| **Mr Woodman** | Looks like they were right. You *are* greedy. |
| **Johnny** | But what about our fire? It's freezing cold. |
| **Mr Woodman** | You'll have to change your ways, won't you? Come on, Logs. |
| **Logs and Mr Woodman** | Bye bye. |
| | *(Exit Mr Woodman followed by Logs.)* |
| **Johnny** | Come on, let's have something to eat. That'll make us warm. |
| | *(Exit Greedylumps.)* |
| **Narrator** | Now let's see what happens to the Grumpydumps.... |

## Scene III

*Enter Grumpydumps and spread out on stage in different positions and at different levels ready to do various jobs in their workshop such as hammering, painting and sawing. Off stage percussion players play 'Grumpydumps' work piece' (see page 142) while Grumpydumps do their jobs in time with the music. Extend this section by playing the piece through more than once while workers change jobs or swop places or all participate in the same job.*

**Grumpydumps** | *(Sounding very grumpy!)* Work, work, work, work, work, work, work!
Working all day makes you groan! Ugh!
Work, work, work, work, work, work, work
Working all day makes you moan! Oooooooh!
Work, work, work, work, work, work, work
Working your fingers to the bone! Ow!
Work, work, work, work, work, work, work
Working all day makes you.... *(Shout and stamp.)* extremely grumpy!

| | |
|---|---|
| **Grumpydump 1** | I'm freezing. |
| **Grumpydump 2** | So am I. |
| **Grumpydump 3** | I wish we had a fire. |
| **Grumpydump 4** | Who forgot to get the logs? |
| **Grumpydump 5** | Him! I expect. *(Elbowing another Grumpydump.)* |
| **Grumpydump 6** | Huh! It's always my fault, isn't it? |

| | |
|---|---|
| | *(Knock at door is heard.)* |
| **Grumpydumps** | What do you want? Come in if you have to. You don't have to break the door down you know. |
| | *(Improvise other similar bad-tempered responses.)* |
| | *(Enter Mr Woodman.)* |
| **Mr Woodman** | I wondered if you wanted any wood. |
| **Grumpydumps** | Yes. |
| **Mr Woodman** | Yes *please.* |
| **Grumpydumps** | *(Very grumpily.)* Yes please. |
| **Mr Woodman** | It won't work if you're grumpy you know. |
| **Grumpydumps** | Grumpy? Rubbish! Stupid thing to say. Nobody's grumpy round here.... *(Improvise with other similar comments too.)* |
| **Mr Woodman** | Let's see. |
| **Grumpydumps and Mr Woodman** | Logger logger lie down<br>Lie down low.<br>Logger logger lie down<br>And make the fire go. |
| | *(One log lies down. Repeat the verse as each log lies down.)* |
| **Grumpydump 1** | I'll light it. |
| **Grumpydump 2** | No, I'll light it. |
| **Grumpydump 3** | No, I'll light it. |
| **Grumpydump 4** | No, I'll light it. *(Meanwhile Mr Woodman calmly lights it.)* |
| **Mr Woodman** | I've already lit it and it's not working. That's because you're all so grumpy. |
| **Grumpydump 1** | Well what about our fire? |
| **Mr Woodman** | Tough! Come on, Logs. *(Exit Mr Woodman and Logs.)* |
| **Grumpydumps** | Bad tempered old stick. |
| | *(All exit.)* |
| **Narrator** | Now let's see what happens to the Lazyslumps.... |

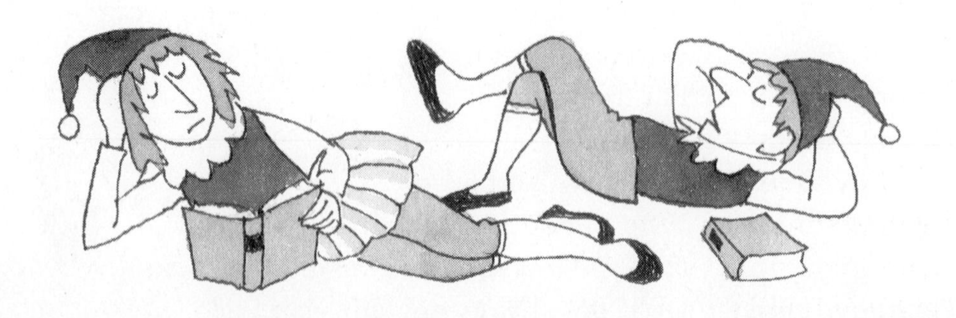

# Scene IV

*Enter the Lazyslumps assuming casual, comfortable, reclining poses. Each one is occupied in a gentle activity such as looking in a mirror, combing hair, doing nails, reading, but all look exhausted.*

**Lazyslump 1** This is absolutely exhausting.

**Lazyslump 2** So is this.

**Lazyslump 3** Pass my book someone. *(Book is passed along line with exaggerated exertion.)*

*(All cast sing 'Lazyslumps' song' [see page 142].*

*Then a knock at the door is heard.)*

**Lazyslump 1** *(To Lazyslump 2.)* Answer that, would you?

**Lazyslump 2** *(To Lazyslump 3.)* Answer that, would you?

**Lazyslump 3** *(To Lazyslump 4.)* Answer that, would you?

*(This continues until all the Lazyslumps have been asked.)*

*(Enter Mr Woodman and Logs.)*

**Mr Woodman** Everybody's too lazy to answer the door I see. Well, it doesn't look like *you're* going to get a nice warm fire.

**Lazyslumps** Why not?

**Mr Woodman** Because the logs won't burn for lazy people.

**Lazyslump 1** Yes they will.

**Lazyslump 2** Just be a dear and make the fire, would you Mr Woodman?

**Mr Woodman** Logger logger lie down,
Lie down low.
Logger logger lie down
And make the fire go.

*(First log lies down. Repeat this verse as each log lies down.)*

**Lazyslump 3** Perhaps we should all blow on it.

**Lazyslumps** No, no that's far too exhausting.

**Mr Woodman** It wouldn't do any good anyway because you're all too lazy. Come on Logs, let's go. *(Mr Woodman and Logs exit.)*

*(Knock on door.)*

# Scene V

*Another knock on door is heard in the Lazyslumps' cottage.*

**All Lazyslumps** Come in.

*(Enter all Grumpydumps.)*

**Grumpydump 1** Got any wood?

| | |
|---|---|
| **Lazyslump 1** | Don't be so rude. You should say, I'm sorry to bother you but have you by any chance got any wood that you would be kind enough to lend us? |
| **Grumpydump 1** | Well, have you? |
| **Lazyslump 2** | Even if we had, it wouldn't work for you because you're too grumpy. |
| **Grumpydump 3** | Well, at least we're not lazy. We walked here. |
| **Lazyslump 4** | Well, we were just going for a walk. |
| **Lazyslump 5** | Yes, come on. Let's go. |
| **Grumpydumps** | Can *we* come? |
| **Lazyslump 5** | We don't walk with grumpy people. |
| **Grumpydumps** | *(Break into wide grins!)* Pleeeeeeease.... |
| **Lazyslumps** | OK. |
| | *(All Lazyslumps and Grumpydumps exit.)* |

## Scene VI

*Enter Greedylumps. Two Grumpydumps bring on a tree. All start hanging up decorations on the tree.*

| | |
|---|---|
| **Johnny** | Right, time for a break. I'll get a snack. |
| | *(Johnny exits then hurries back looking very worried.)* |
| **Johnny** | Oh no, we've run out of food. |
| **Jenny** | But where's the Christmas dinner gone? |
| **Jimmy** | We ate it yesterday, remember? |
| **Greedylumps** | Oh no! |
| | *(Knock at door is heard.)* |
| **Greedylumps** | *(Sadly.)* Come in. |
| | *(Enter Grumpydumps grinning widely.)* |
| **Grumpydumps** | You lot look grumpy. |
| **Greedylumps** | You lot look happy. |
| **Grumpydumps** | *(Still grinning.)* Happy Christmas. |
| | *(Enter Lazyslumps.)* |
| **Lazyslumps** | Happy Christmas everybody. |
| **Lazyslump 1** | Want some help decorating the tree? |
| | *(Greedylumps nod miserably and stay seated while all others on stage help decorate tree. Then enter Mr Woodman followed by Logs.)* |
| **Mr Woodman** | Happy Christmas everybody. We've brought some lovely goodies to eat. |
| | *(Greedylumps stay quite still, but all the others say 'Lovely, thank you' and so on.)* |
| **Log 1** | I see Greedylumps. |
| **Log 2** | Not eating. |

| | |
|---|---|
| **Log 3** | That means they're not greedy! |
| **Log 4** | I see Lazyslumps. |
| **Log 5** | They must have walked here. |
| **Log 6** | That means they're not lazy. |
| **Log 7** | I see Grumpydumps. |
| **Log 8** | They're smiling. |
| **Log 9** | That means they're not grumpy. |
| | *(If you have fewer Logs, double speeches.)* |
| **Mr Woodman** | Right, let's try a fire. I'll need lots of help. |
| | *(Enter rest of cast. Flames form a semicircle behind other characters.)* |
| **All Cast** | Logger logger lie down, lie down low. |
| | Logger logger lie down and make the fire go. |
| | *(Repeat for each Log as before. Flames leap up from below stage – or as close as possible to Logs if stage is not raised. Flames stretch and crouch and leap and turn; experiment with arm movements to make fire dance. All cast, except Flames, shout out 'hurray!' as soon as Flames appear then as Flames settle into flickering, less dynamic actions, all cast call out 'Happy Christmas' and wave to the audience.)* |

Ann Bryant

# Lord of the dance

*This is a Nativity-based music and dance drama for infants and/or lower juniors. The play consists of five scenes, referred to as tableaux: angels, shepherds, animals, kings and queens, and children.*

*As many or as few children as you want can take part in each tableau. There should be a small Singing Group on a separate part of the stage or on a bench below the stage. This group sings each verse of the theme song to link the action of the different tableaux. The theme song is based on 'The Lord of the Dance' by Sydney Carter with adapted lyrics. The music for this and the other songs written for the performance can be found on pages 134 to 138. You may also want to use additional carols for each tableau.*

*There could also be a Percussion Group which can accompany all of the songs and music.*

*The suggestions for choreography given for each tableau can be easily adapted to suit particular situations.*

**All**

***Verse 1***
**I danced in the morning when the world was begun**
**And I danced in the moon and the stars and the sun**
**I came down from heaven and I danced on the earth**
**At Bethlehem I had my birth.**

***Chorus***
**Dance then wherever you may be**
**I am the Lord of the Dance said he**
**And I'll lead you all wherever you may be**
**And I'll lead you all in the dance said he.**

**Singing Group**

***Verse 2***
**I danced in the angels when they spread their wings**
**And they lit up the sky to make everybody sing**
**They flew down to tell the shepherds what to do**
**A baby King, yes, yes it's true.**

***Chorus***

**First tableau: angels**

Angels dance on to the stage through the audience. Use recorded music such as 'The Aviary' from *Carnival of the Animals* by Saint-Saëns or an extract from Mendelssohn's *Midsummer Night's Dream*, or any magical or mystical sounding music to accompany them.

Once on the stage the angels should stand in a line across the front of the stage. They should all bend down, then, while stretching slowly up again, roll their hands over and over each other until they are standing up straight. They should then open their arms and look up. They should repeat this movement four times.

The children should slowly sway four times with their arms above their heads and slowly sway four times with their arms down low.

One angel should remain in the centre of the stage with wings spread, while the others run (fairy like) around him. They should circle the stage twice in each direction and finish in a circle. The central angel should then join the circle. Standing in the circle, the angels should bend down and then sway slowly as before.

One angel should lead the others (fairy footsteps) round the stage once and then into line and kneel in a praying position.

**Angels**

As the shepherds watched their sheep on that starry, starry night,
They could hear the angels' song,
They could see the angels' light.
Sing angels, sing angels,
Sing your song for them,
Shine angels, shine angels, shine your light on them.
(*See page 136 for the music for 'Angel song'.*)

All the characters in this tableau should then leave the stage to the accompaniment of the 'Angel song' and the shepherds should enter and assemble on the stage.

**Singing Group**

***Verse 3***
**I danced in the shepherds as they watched their sheep**
**Although they were tired they just couldn't go to sleep.**
**They flew down to tell the shepherds what to do,**
**A baby King, yes, yes it's true.**
***Chorus***

**Second tableau: shepherds**

Choose any country dance music with an obvious rhythm of eight beats. Have two or three tambourine players, placed to the side of the dancers. Four pairs of shepherds four boys and four girls should be positioned on stage as shown below.

**B G**      **B G**

**B G**             **B G**

(B = Boy
G = Girl)

Each pair should hold both their partner's hands and skip round in a circle for eight counts and then skip in the other direction for eight more. The boys should kneel on one knee and strike their other thighs, while the girls side-step and skip round their partners for eight counts. The girls should then stand still and clap, while the boys side-step and skip round them for eight counts.

All the children should form a circle and clap (this should take eight counts). Then the whole circle should side step, while holding hands, in one direction for eight counts and then in the other direction for eight counts.

The children should open out into a line so that they are facing the audience. They should take about eight counts to do this, clapping to the rhythm at the same time. If all eight counts are not used for this manoeuvre they should stand still, in their line, and continue clapping. The boys, in their line, should bob down into a crouched position as the girls stretch their arms up high. Then the girls should crouch down while the boys stretch up. The children should do this to four beats and repeat the movement three times. They can then hold both their partner's hands and skip round in a circle for eight counts one way and eight counts the other way.

Finally, the boys should bow and the girls curtsey to each other for four counts, bow and curtsey to the audience for four counts and leave the stage.

**Singing Group** | ***Verse 4***
**I danced in the animals, the cat, the mouse,**
**The goat and the cow that let Jesus share their house**
**They lay down beside the baby, soft and new,**
**A baby King, yes, yes it's true.**
***Chorus***

**Third tableau: animals**

Enter children pretending to be animals.

**Animals** | *Verse 1*
The cows looked at the baby and said 'Moo moo moo'.
The cows looked at the baby and said 'Moo moo moo'.
'Moo moo moo'.
Moo moo moo'.
The cows looked at the baby and said, 'Moo moo moo'.
*Verse 2*
The sheep looked at the baby and said, 'Baa baa baa'.
*Verse 3*
The pigs looked at the baby and said, 'Oink oink oink'.
*Verse 4*
The dogs looked at the baby and said, 'Woof woof woof'.
*Verse 5*
The cat looked at the baby and said, 'Miaow miaow miaow'.
*Verse 6*
The mice looked at the baby and said, 'Squeak squeak squeak'.
(*See page 137 for the music for 'Animal song'.*)

It is a good idea to involve the youngest children in this tableau. They should make the relevant animal noises and imitate the various animal movements . The children can also wear masks if you like. Let them repeat the song so that the animals have a chance to show their movement and noise from on stage. The animals should then regroup to create a different tableau. Finally, they can all exit to the accompaniment of the song.

| | |
|---|---|
| **Singing Group** | ***Verse 5***<br>**I danced in the Kings and Queens who travelled far.**<br>**They followed the light of the great big silver star.**<br>**They came to the stable and their happiness grew**<br>**A baby King, yes yes it's true.**<br>***Chorus*** |

**Fourth tableau: kings and queens**

The percussion players should play the 'Kings' and queens' song' slowly while the kings and queens enter.

| | |
|---|---|
| **Kings and Queens** | Queens, Queens, Queens from the East!<br>Queens, Queens, Queens from the East!<br>We have brought many gifts on our journey so far,<br>We have travelled at night by the light of the star.<br>Queens, Queens, Queens from the East!<br>Kings, Kings, Kings from the East!<br>Kings, Kings, Kings from the East!<br>We have brought many gifts on our journey so far,<br>We have travelled at night by the light of the star.<br>Kings, Kings, Kings from the East!<br>*(See page 138 for the music to the 'Kings' and queens' song'.)* |

The kings and queens should position themselves on stage as shown below:

| 3rd | 3rd | | | | 2nd | 2nd |
|---|---|---|---|---|---|---|
| Q | K | | | | Q | K |
| | | 1st | 1st | | | |
| | | Q | K | | | |

Use the music from the 'Arab Dance' from *Peer Gynt Suite* by Grieg to accompany the following dance. After the first four beats the first king should move first his right and then his left arm in a 'look at this' gesture. He should then bow to his queen who makes the same gesture and then curtseys. The king then bows again to his queen who curtseys and then they bow to each other.

The second queen should walk up to the first king and curtsey and the third king should walk to the first queen and bow. The second king walks and bows to the second queen and the third queen walks and curtseys to the third king leaving each king and queen back with their own partners.

Each king and queen should face each other and raise their right arms high and clasp their partner's right hands with their right hands. In this position they should walk round in a circle for 12 beats. They should then repeat this, but this time clasp their left hands and moving in the other direction.

The couples should assume the traditional 'escorting' hand position with the queen placing her hand palm down over the king's hand, which is also palm down. All three couples should turn to their right

and process 'regally' round the stage for 24 beats, returning to their original positions.

The first king and queen should take two large steps backwards and the other kings and queens can join them (one couple on either side) using dainty steps, but the same amount of music. The first king takes two large steps forwards and the other kings then join him, taking smaller steps, but the same amount of music.

For the next 16 beats all the kings and queens should do the following hand sequence:

- right arm 'look at this gesture';
- left arm 'look at this gesture';
- right hand on waist;
- left hand on waist;
- right arm up;
- left arm up;
- both hands 'put crowns on head' gesture;
- both arms at sides.

Then all three kings should kneel on one leg for eight beats, while the queens dance round their kings and the kings beat their right thighs in time with music.

For the last eight beats the kings and queens should assume the positions that they started in and then all bow and curtsey to the audience and leave the stage.

Let the music run to the end of 'Arab Dance' as the children for the next tableau come down the central aisle through the audience and up on to the stage. Mary and Joseph enter from side with crib. The children should form a semi-circle round Mary and Joseph.

**Singing Group** | ***Verse 6***
**I danced in the children as they smiled and sang**
**All over the world bells of glory glory rang.**
**The children danced and the world danced too.**
**A baby King, yes yes it's true.**
***Chorus***

### Fifth tableau: children

Let the children sing the well-known Christmas Carol, 'In the Bleak Mid-Winter', they can be accompanied by the percussion group. Let each child skip, walk or dance round the stage holding a present and then stop at the crib, bend down and give the present to Jesus. The last child should sing the last verse of the carol and give Jesus a lamb.

This tableau should remain on the stage while the characters from the other four tableaux come on stage or stand anywhere in the hall where they can be seen. During this, the accompaniment to 'I danced in the morning' should be played. When all the children are assembled, everyone should sing 'I danced in the morning'. Encourage the audience to join in with the chorus.

Ann Bryant

# A boy is born

*Any number of narrators can take part in this nativity play. Other children can act out the story and join in with the carols.*

**First child**

Tell me friend, what's going on?
Why do these people stare,
Outside this lowly stable?
Is something happening there?

We could not sleep, though we had passed
A hard and tiring day,
Then something made us leave our beds,
And made us come this way.

There's a feeling in the air tonight,
And see that star – it's far more bright,
Than any I have seen.
My blood flows warm, my heart feels glad,
Although this world is cold and sad,
So what can all this mean?

**Second child**

A hundred people standing here,
Are whispering the same,
A hundred people watching,
And on their lips a name.

So sing a song of angels,
Tell the story from the start,
A new young bride called Mary,
A longing in her heart.
*(All sing the carol 'Mary, Mary'.)*

**Third child**

The angel brought the young girl news,
And to her lips a smile.
She would, before the year was out,
Be mother to a child.

**Fourth child**

But they tell me that this couple
Lived many miles away,

So why are they in Bethlehem
Upon this winter's day?

**Third child** The State's declared a census
Of people high and low,
And all men, including Joseph,
To their place of birth must go.

And though his wife was great with child,
And its time was surely near,
With their bedding and a donkey,
They had to travel here.
*(All sing the carol 'Little Donkey'.)*

**Fifth child** I've not seen so many people,
In Bethlehem before.
They say you'll make some money,
If you rent someone your floor!

Rich men and their servants,
Rushing here and there,
All trying to find shelter,
From the icy desert air.

**Sixth child** The inns are overflowing.
I'd almost stake my life,
There'd be no empty rooms left
For a poor man and his wife.
*(All sing the carol 'There Isn't Any Room'.)*

**Seventh child** The gently smiling mother,
The father watching there,
A tiny, new-born baby,
But is this something rare?

For many infant boys are born,
And many are born poor,
So why is it I feel that here
We witness something more?

**Eighth child** But look again, the air is filled
With glowing, golden light!

And it seems that angel voices
Lift the darkness from the night.

My spirit soars to heaven,
My heart is filled with joy,
For there I see the Son of God,
Not just a little boy.
*(All sing the carol 'It Was on a Starry Night'.)*

**Ninth child** But is this the king they spoke of
So many years before,
Who would come to help the suffering,
The needy and the poor?

**Tenth child** Can we be sure that this is Him?
He wears no crown of gold.
The prophets had no tales of wealth,
But this is what they told:

**Ninth child** That we would know he'd come to us,
For there would be a sign,
So look into the heavens,
And see that bright star shine.
*(All sing the carol 'Star Blaze'.)*

**Eleventh child** They say a little later
Three men came to that place,
They begged to see the new-born King,
And – gazing at his face

**Twelfth child** Rejoiced – the long-awaited
Had come at last to Earth.
But they'd been sleeping on the hillside,
Who told them of this birth?
*(All sing the carol 'Come They Told Me'.)*

**Thirteenth child** I've heard amazing rumours
That in distant lands from these,
This bright new star's been noticed,
Over deserts, hills and seas.

And many people wonder,
And many people fear,
And three great Kings who saw it
Are following it here.

They've journeyed through the burning sun,
And through the dawn's grey cold,
To see this child and bring him myrrh,
And frankincense and gold.
*(All sing the carol 'Lift up Lightly the Stable Bar' or 'We Three Kings'.)*

**Fourteenth child** So the child is born; one day the man
Will come to us with outstretched hand
And guide all those who want to hear his call,
Though evil will not disappear,
And nor will envy, hate and fear,
Yet we will have the strength to face them all.

The little child is sleeping still,
Quite safe from those who'd wish him ill,
So look once more upon this wondrous sight
And when two thousand years have passed,
And all of you are born at last,
Remember us, and what we saw tonight.
*(All sing the carol 'Ding Dong Merrily'.)*

**Fifteenth child** We've told the story of a boy,
Who came to Earth to bring us joy,
And if it's touched your hearts our task is done.
So there's only one thing left to say,
Before you travel on your way,
A very Happy Christmas everyone!
*(All sing the carol 'We Wish You a Merry Christmas'.)*

Diana Jones

# Quick Christmas performances

*Often there is very little time available at the end of term to rehearse and stage a school production. Here, however, are two simple performance ideas, based on popular Christmas stories.*

## Jack and the beanstalk

*This production can be divided so that whole classes or year groups are each responsible for a different segment. Each segment can be enhanced by art, craft, dance and music work which has already been completed in class. Having completed the background work during the term, it may be that only two weeks are needed to rehearse and bring together the various segments.*

### Characters

Jack (wearing coloured, woollen tights; loose sweater, tied at the waist with a belt); Mother (wearing a long dress or long skirt and blouse; small white apron; mop cap); Giant and Cow (both wearing suitable masks).

### Main story

Begin the story of Jack and the beanstalk in the traditional way with poor Mother sending Jack to market to sell their only cow and Jack returning with three magic beans and growing an enormous beanstalk.

As Jack climbs the beanstalk he can step off into three different countries to find the people celebrating their own festivals. These could be done in the form of a series of tableaux.

### Tableau 1: Chinese New Year

The children can wear loose tops over trousers and coolie shaped hats. Several children can work together to form a dragon, with one wearing a dragon mask.

### Tableau 2: Hanukah

The children can wear long tunics tied at the waist with sashes. The scene could include the lighting of candles in the menorak.

### Tableau 3: Diwali

The boys can wear coloured shirts and trousers; bright sashes draped over one shoulder and hold candles. The girls can wear saris or brightly-coloured dresses with bright sashes draped over one shoulder. They could also wear bracelets and necklaces and hold candles.

Rama and Ravana can wear turbans like crowns, and Hanuman, the monkey king, could wear a monkey-faced mask.

### Ending

Once each tableau has been visited Jack can arrive at the top of the beanstalk where he sneaks into the Giant's castle and steals the magic harp and the goose which lays the golden eggs. Finally, after chopping down the beanstalk and killing the giant, the last scene can show Jack and Mother sharing a traditional Christmas scene at home.

**Resources**

- 'Jack and the Beanstalk' by Douglas Coombes in *Time and Tune*, Autumn 1979 (BBC).
- *Festivals*, Jean Gilbert (Oxford University Press).
- *Every Colour Under the Sun; A Music Calendar of Festivals; The Singing Sack; The Tinderbox* (A & C Black).
- *Dragon Boat*, Gaik See Chew (Chester Music).
- *Junior Education*, October 1987 – Festivals.
- *Junior Education*, March 1987 – China.
- *Junior Projects*, No 46 – Celebrations.
- *Infant Projects*, No 67 – Decoration.
- *Exploring Religious Festivals*, Olivia Bennett (Bell & Hyman).

Recorded music (to be played as audience arrives):

- *Carol Symphony*, Hely-Hutchinson.
- *Mother Goose Suite*, Ravel.

# Baboushka

*This performance could be a simple re-enactment of the story, accompanied by the children singing songs and carols.*

**Characters**

Village girls and Baboushka (wearing brightly coloured skirts; white blouses; white paper or cotton aprons; white knee socks; black shoes; headscarves), Village boys (wearing 'too-big' open-necked shirts worn over trousers and tied at the waist with belts; neckerchieves; wellington boots worn over trousers), Kings (wearing crowns and robes), Star, Angels, Mary, Joseph, Shepherds.

**Scene 1**

Star enters and everyone sings 'Twinkle, Twinkle Little Star'. The Villagers see the Star and celebrate with dancing. They can clap and dance to 'Kalinka'. Finally, the Star settles by Baboushka's cottage to the sound of tinkling on metal instruments.

**Scene 2**

Three Kings visit Baboushka's cottage. She gives them what little food she has and they invite Baboushka to help them find the Baby. She is too busy, so refuses. All the children sing 'Follow the Star'.

**Scene 3**

The Star leads the Kings out to the sound of tinkling on metal instruments. However, Baboushka decides to follow them and all the children sing 'How Far Is It to Bethlehem?'

**Scene 4**

The Star leads the Kings to some Shepherds who also follow the Star to

the stable. The children then sing 'Away in a Manger'. Also in the stable are Mary, Joseph and the Angels.

**Scene 5**

Mary, Joseph, the Angels, Kings and Shepherds all leave the stable to 'Child for the World'. Once they've all left, Baboushka arrives. The children sing 'Now It's Christmas' as Baboushka gives them her presents.

**Resources**

- 'Twinkle Twinkle, Little Star', *Someone's Singing, Lord* (A & C Black).
- 'Kalinka', *More Songs for Singing Together* (BBC Publications).
- 'Follow the Star', *Baboushka* (Cassell).
- 'How Far is it to Bethlehem?', *Carol, Gaily Carol* (A & C Black).
- 'Away in a Manger', *Songs of Praise.*
- 'Child for the World', *Festivals* (Oxford University Press).
- 'Now It's Christmas', *Christmas Songs to Sing* (E.J. Arnold).

Lynn Dolby

# The Christmas birthday

*This play can be performed in modern dress, with Mary, Joseph and the two Shepherds dressed simply, the three Wise Men in smart outfits with bow ties, and the Angel looking flashy in white.*

*For the first part of the play the stable, which can be as simple as a few bales of straw and a crib, should remain hidden.*

**Characters**

Mary, Joseph, two Shepherds, three Wise Men and a street-wise Angel.

## Scene I

*The Angel enters, and talks to audience.*

**Angel** Hi. I'm an angel. God sent me down here to search for a girl. 'Her name's Mary,' He said. Very helpful. Anyway, with some divine help I finally found her, and proceeded to tell her the good news. 'Guess what?' I said, after she had got over the shock of seeing me appear on her doorstep. 'Guess what? You're going to have a baby – and he's going to change the world.' She was surprised, I can tell you.
Well, now God tells me that Mary is going to have her little baby any time now... and in a cowshed! I think God could have done better than that – but quite honestly he has a habit of always being right. I've been sent to find some people to go along and meet Mary and her husband Joseph and see the newborn baby. *(Counts on fingers.)* I have to find two shepherds, and three wise men. So, I can't stand here talking all day... must fly. *(Hears voices.)* Here's a bit of luck. If I'm not very much mistaken, the two people coming this way are shepherds. Don't be surprised if they don't see me right away – angels are full of tricks like that.
*(Puts fingers to his lips as two Shepherds enter.)*

**Shepherd 1** *(Looks at audience.)* Flock's looking good today.

**Shepherd 2** Not bad. *(Stares back at audience.)* That one could do with a bit of shearing.

**Shepherd 1** Yes. It's good being a shepherd, isn't it?

**Shepherd 2** Oh yes. Being a shepherd? I love it.

**Shepherd 1** I wouldn't be anything else but a shepherd.

**Shepherd 2** Nor me. It's a shepherd's life for me.
*(The Angel jumps up, and the Shepherds see the Angel for the first time.)*

**Angel** You're shepherds, aren't you?

**Shepherd 1** Yes. How did you guess?

**Angel** Never mind that. Now listen to me. You're to follow a star. *(Points to star at back of stage.)* That one.

**Shepherd 2** Why? And who are you?

**Angel** I'm an angel, sent by God, so you'd better do as I say.

**Shepherd 1** Prove it.

**Angel** No time. Come on.

**Shepherd 2** But what about our sheep?

**Angel** They'll be all right.

**Shepherd 1** And what about.... *(Angel ushers them off stage.)*

**Angel** Well, that wasn't too bad. But wise men? That could be more difficult. Any here? *(Stares into audience.)* No.

*(Unannounced the three Wise Men enter, arguing about wise things. The Angel crouches in the shadows.)*

**Wise Man 1** No, no. Bethlehem is much further than that. Population two hundred. No gas in the village.

**Wise Man 2** Precisely. But if you take the square root of 81, you get 9.

**Wise Man 3** So what?

**Wise Man 2** I don't know.

**Wise Man 1** I feel quite weary. I've been wise all day, without stopping.

**Wise Man 2** Not even for lunch?

**Wise Man 1** No. Too many calories. Did you know that an average size jacket potato has 120 calories?

**Wise Man 3** Is that with or without butter?

*(Angel stands before them.)*

**Angel** Excuse me. I'm an angel and you are, if I'm not mistaken, three extremely wise men.

**Wise Men** *(Together.)* Correct.

**Angel** In that case, would you do something for me? Well, for God, really.

**Wise Man 1** This is the oddest thing that has ever happened to me.

**Wise Man 2** With all my wiseness, I can't understand it.

**Wise Man 3** True. But I think it would be wise to listen.

**Angel** Right. This is it. There is a baby to be born in Bethlehem....

**Wise Man 2** We were just talking about....

**Angel** Angel Shh. Listen. A baby, to be born in Bethlehem. He's to be the Son of God, and he will change the world, making it better, for ever more.

**Wise Man 3** How?

| | |
|---|---|
| **Angel** | Wait and see. I have been instructed by God to find three wise men, like you, to visit this baby, and his parents, Mary and Joseph. |
| **Wise Man 1** | And? |
| **Angel** | That's it. |
| **Wise Man 3** | What? Just turn up to visit? Won't they be terribly busy? What with a new baby and what must be an enormous place to run? |
| **Angel** | It won't be a palace, not even an inn. The baby was going to be born in an inn, but there wasn't any room – so he is being born in the stable outside instead. |
| **Wise Man 2** | But it's not possible. Why should the Son of God be born in an old stable? |
| **Wise Man 1** | Maybe it's to show everyone else that money isn't everything – and faith is a little more important. I vote we should go. |
| **Wise Man 3** | Well, OK. But we can't just turn up. We'll have to take something. |
| **Wise Man 2** | Gifts! |
| **Wise Man 3** | Exactly. I'll take some myrhh. |
| **Wise Man 1** | Myrrh? What on earth's that? |
| **Wise Man 2** | A resin from trees, used in perfume and medicine. |
| **Wise Man 3** | Precisely! very good. |
| **Wise Man 1** | I'll take some gold. It's easier. He'll love it. |
| **Wise Man 2** | And I'll take some frankincense. |
| **Wise Man 1** | Fran...? |
| **Wise Man 2** | *(Pats Wise Man 1 on the shoulder.)* An aromatic gum. Don't worry about it. Stick with your gold. |
| **Angel** | Ready? |
| **Wise Men** | Certainly. |
| **Angel** | Follow the star! |
| | *(All exit.)* |

# Scene II

*The scene changes to the stable where Mary and Joseph are tending the baby Jesus.*

| | |
|---|---|
| **Mary** | He's going to be so handsome. |
| **Joseph** | Well yes, but.... |
| **Mary** | His name will be Jesus. |
| **Joseph** | That's a very nice name. But why... shh. What's that noise? Is someone coming? |
| **Mary** | Probably just the horses, or the sheep, or maybe be the cows. Don't worry. |

**Joseph** Well, I feel I've let you down. First that long donkey ride, and then when we got here there was no room at the inn. You must be so tired.

**Mary** I'm fine. I'm happy. I love you and I love baby Jesus. What more do I need?

**Joseph** *(Jumps up.)* There is someone there. Who comes?

*(Shepherds voices off.)*

**Shepherds** Only us.

**Shepherd 1** Two humble shepherds come to meet you and your baby.

**Shepherd 2** Can we come in?

**Joseph** *(To Mary.)* All right?

**Mary** Of course. Come in, and not so much of the humble.

*(Shepherds enter and look down at the baby. Slowly they take of their caps. Their faces are lit by a light hidden in the crib.)*

**Shepherd 1** He's beautiful.

**Shepherd 2** He *is* the Son of God. Even as a simple shepherd, I bless Him and praise Him.

**Mary** Thank you. He will be a shepherd too. He will be the good shepherd for all the people in the world.

**Joseph** Will he? That's wonderful. Have you travelled far?

**Shepherd 1** We can't remember. An angel appeared and told us to follow that star.

**Shepherd 2** So we did.

**Shepherd 1** We thought we'd better.

**Shepherd 2** But we're glad we came. Can we stay for a while?

**Joseph** Of course. *(He beckons them to sit – as they do, the three Wise Men enter.)*

**Wise Man 1** Sorry to disturb you. May we come in?

**Mary** Who are you?

**Wise Man 2** We're three wise men from the Orient and we were....

**Joseph** Sent by an angel.

**Wise Man 3** How did you know?

**Joseph** Just a guess.

**Wise Man 1** Can we see the baby now?

**Mary** Please do.

*(The three Wise Men look into the manger and the light glows on to their faces.)*

**Wise Man 1** Beautiful. He makes me feel humble.

**Shepherd 1** Well, how do you think we felt.

**Mary** In God's eyes, you're all the same. You're all just as important. These three wise man have become wise, but they couldn't tend sheep as you do. To God we're

all children... his children.

*(As the three Wise Men present their gifts, their voices fade away as they say lines such as 'We've brought gold for the baby', 'We have travelled far to meet him', 'This Frankincense is specially for him.' As the group mime conversation, the Angel walks on and talks to the audience.)*

**Angel** And that's how it all happened. I think I did pretty well choosing that lot. The baby's got an incredible life in front of him. He will perform miracles. He'll cure the sick. Thousands of people will gather round him just to listen to him speak. He'll be a good son to God – so much so, that, for thousands of years people will talk about him, remember him, and praise him. And what he'll leave behind is a lot of goodness and a lot of faith – and that's what this old world will need. Anyway, don't forget his name, Jesus. You're really privileged. You were there, at the beginning of his life. And I arranged all that for you. Leave it to me. It's easy... for an angel.

*(The angel winks and walks off.)*

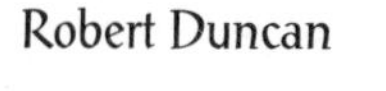
Robert Duncan

# The master of the time vortex and his magic Christmas show

*This play has 36 speaking parts and 6 dance parts. It is set in the present day and the action takes place at the North Pole, and in the living room at the Thins' house. Music and sound effects, pre-recorded on to tape, will add significantly to the atmosphere of the play.*

**Characters**

Mrs Thin, Granny Thin, Tom Thin, Jerry Thin, Susan Thin, Master of the Time Vortex, Helper 1, Helper 2, three Witches, Wizard, Chief Crazy Horse, Red Feet, six Indian Braves, Long Johns, Dirty-Hands George, Black Doggy, Billy the Rum, Yellowdog Pete, four Pirates, Santa Claus, two Clerks, three Audience Voices, Stage Manager, six Star Dancers.

## Scene 1

*The North Pole. The wind is blowing, snow is falling. The Master's two Helpers enter.*

**Helper 1** Where *is* the Master of the Time Vortex?
**Helper 2** He should be here by now.
**Helper 1** He's so absent-minded.
**Helper 2** Well, if he doesn't arrive soon, he'll be too late to collect the key.
**Helper 1** Wait, here he comes.
**Helper 2** About time too!
**Master** *(Entering)* I'm not late, am I?
**Helper 1** Just in time, Master.
**Master** Good. However, I *am* the Master of the Time Vortex, so I can be late if I wish.
**Helper 2** But you mustn't be late for Santa Claus.
**Helper 1** You have to collect the key from him.
**Master** Key? Oh, the key!
**Helpers** The key to open the Time Vortex.
**Master** Of course, the key. I almost forgot!
**Helper 1** Have you got the silver medallion?
*(The Master finds it his pocket.)*
**Helper 2** Have you got the golden snake?
*(The Master finds it on a chain around his neck.)*
**Helpers** Then we're ready to go in.
**Master** Go in? Go in where?

**Helper 1** | To collect the key from Santa Claus!
**Helper 2** | Before it's too late!
**Helpers** | Come on, Master, come on. We must get the key! *(They exit. Wind howls.)*

# Scene II

*The office of Santa Claus, the North Pole. Two Clerks enter and take their places at a reception table. They check through various lists and papers.*

**Clerk 1** | He's late, as usual.
**Clerk 2** | Who? Who's late?
**Clerk 1** | The Master of the Time Vortex.
**Clerk 2** | He's always late. He was last year.
**Clerk 1** | He'd better arrive soon, or he'll miss Santa Claus.
**Clerk 2** | Have you got the key?
**Clerk 1** | Yes, it's here. *(Loud knocking.)* What on earth is that? *(Clerk 2 opens the door. Wind howls.)*
**Clerk 2** | Come in, come in, you're late, you know.
**Helper 1** | *(Entering.)* The Master...
**Helper 2** | *(Entering.)* of the Time Vortex....
**Helper 1** | apologises...
**Helper 2** | for being late.
**Helper 1** | The Master...
**Helper 2** | has come to collect the key.
**Master** | *(Entering and pushing the helpers aside.)* Oh, get on with it, you two! It's the key I'm after, I want the key.
**Clerk 1** | First, you must identify yourself.
**Helper 1** | The Master has the silver medallion. *(It is displayed.)*
**Helper 2** | And he has the golden snake. *(It is displayed.)*
**Master** | And now I'll have the key, please.
**Clerk 2** | You'll have to see Santa Claus for that.
**Clerk 1** | I'll see if he is free. *(He exits.)*
**Clerk 2** | Now remember, Master of the Time Vortex, don't keep Santa Claus messing about. Don't delay him. He's very, very, very busy. It *is* Christmas Eve, after all.
**Santa Claus** | *(Entering noisily, with Clerk 1.)* What's this, eh? Who's this all done up like a dog's dinner?
**Clerks** | The Master of the Time Vortex.
**Santa Claus** | Oh, him!
**Master** | Yes, it's me. I want my key.
**Santa Claus** | Late, aren't you? You deserve to be fed on prunes for a week. Has he identified himself?

**Clerks** | He has.
**Master** | So, what about the key?
**Clerk 2** | Here's the box with all the family names inside.
**Clerk 1** | Just dip in and take your pick.
*(Master fumbles in the large box. He eventually withdraws a card.)*
**Master** | Ah ha! The name is....
**Helpers** | Who is it? Who?
**Master** | Patience... the family is the Thins. That's the name on the card... the Thins.
**Clerk 1** | And here is the key to unlock the Time Vortex. *(Hands over a large, gold key.)*
**Master** | That's what I want. Now I can unlock the Time Vortex and bring all the thrills, spills, and Jack and Jills to the family of, who was it, oh yes, the Thins.
**Helpers** | Time we were on our way.
**Santa Claus** | Take great care of that key. Remember, it must be returned to my clerks by six o'clock on Christmas morning.
**Master** | Happy Christmas to you, Santa. Don't get stuck in any chimneys, and don't get your Saint Nickers in a twist! Bye, bye for now.
*(Master and Helpers exit.)*
**Santa Claus** | He's cheeky, that Master.
**Clerk 1** | He grows worse each year.
**Santa Claus** | *(Clapping his hands.)* Now, quick as lightning. Let's get those reindeer filled up with petrol. It's time to begin delivering the presents.
*(Santa Claus and clerks exit. Wind howls.)*

# Scene III

*Living room of the Thins' house. Christmas Eve. The children enter and take their places at the table. Granny Thin sits in a rocking chair. She is knitting.*

**Jerry** | I'm starving. What's for supper?
**Granny** | Don't be rude. Wait, be patient. Your Mother's busy preparing the Christmas dinner.
**Jerry** | That's for tomorrow. I'm hungry now! Just thinking of all that turkey makes me even *more* hungry.
**Tom** | Oh, be quiet, will you? It *is* Christmas Eve, or had you forgotten?
**Jerry** | *(After a pause.)* Funny.
**Tom** | What's funny?
**Jerry** | Christmas Eve.

**Susan** There's nothing funny about Christmas Eve.

**Jerry** Well... it's all too quiet... too quiet for Christmas Eve.

**Granny** Nonsense!

**Jerry** I want something to happen... something exciting!

**Susan** Santa Claus will be coming tonight. Isn't that exciting enough?

**Jerry** Santa Claus! Rubbish!

**Tom** Okay, you two! Don't start arguing. Susan, go help Mum to bring in the supper. *(Susan exits.)*

**Jerry** *(Wandering around the room.)* I still reckon that it's a dead loss, this Christmas Eve nonsense.

**Tom** Stop moaning, Jerry. Come and have a game of chess while we're waiting.

**Jerry** Get lost!

**Granny** Boys, boys, stop it at once. No more complaining and bickering. Please, fetch me my pills, Tom. I want the blue ones not the red ones.

**Tom** Okay, Granny. I'll fetch them. *(Tom exits.)*

**Mrs Thin** Christmas Eve supper! There's cold meat, pickles, bread rolls, ice-cream and tinned strawberries. *(Mrs Thin and Susan lay the food out on the table.)* I hope that everyone is hungry.

**Susan** I am. What a scrumptious lot of grub!

**Granny** You'll be sick, the lot of you. You're called the Thins, but you won't be thin for long if you eat all that food!

**Jerry** I could eat a dinosaur!

**Susan** You *look* like a dinosaur!

**Tom** *(Entering.)* Here are your pills, Granny. The blue ones.

**Granny** Good lad, you can't beat a few good blue pills to set you to rights. Better than tinned strawberries any day.

*(Granny takes her pills – at great length – while the family has supper. She rubs her tummy with evident delight, then hiccups.)*

**Jerry** It still doesn't feel like Christmas Eve.

**Mrs Thin** Cheer up, Jerry. And remember, all of you, no one is to get up before six o'clock tomorrow morning.

**Susan** I'll be awake for hours before that!

**Mrs Thin** Six o'clock is quite early enough, thank you Susan.

**Tom** Last year I woke up at four o'clock.

**Granny** Yes, and woke the whole house, you monkey.

**Jerry** Six o'clock, huh!

**Mrs Thin** Any earlier and you'll probably bump into Santa Claus.

**Jerry** Don't be daft.

**Mrs Thin** | I beg your pardon?
**Jerry** | Er... there's a draft.
**Mrs Thin** | Come on children, finish off. Let's get you up the wooden hill for bed.
**Susan** | I *am* tired.
**Tom** | So am I.
**Mrs Thin** | *(As they all help to clear the table.)* And remember, no one is to wake up before....
**Children** | Six o'clock in the morning! We know!
*(The children exit, followed by Granny.)*
**Mrs Thin** | *(Piling up a tray.)* It's strange, but Jerry is quite right. It *doesn't* quite feel like Christmas Eve. I do wish that something would happen to make it a Christmas to remember. They have been quite good this year, even Jerry. Still, we'll just have to wait and see, just have to wait and see.
*(Mrs Thin exits.)*

## Scene IV

*Church clock strikes three. Wind howling. The Master and his two Helpers arrive outside the Thins' house.*

**Master** | What's the number of that house over there?
**Helper 1** | Number one, Master.
**Master** | Then that's the place, isn't it? That's where the Thins live.
**Helper 2** | *(Checking a sheet of paper.)* Yes, we should find Mrs Thin, Granny, Jerry, Tom, and Susan Thin in there.
**Helper 1** | I suppose that they are in bed by now.
**Master** | Of course they're in bed! It's three o'clock on Christmas morning!
**Helper 2** | Got the Time Vortex key?
**Master** | The key... now where did I put... ah, here it is.
**Helper 1** | We're all ready, then.
**Master** | Let's go inside. Come on, it's cold out here. Listen to that wind. We've just got to say the magic words... now, what were they?
**Helpers** | ALA-KA-ZAZZ! LET US GO INTO THE ROOM!
*(Lights flash. Loud noise. The Master and the Helpers are about to enter the house when a voice is raised in the audience.)*
**Audience Voice 1** | Just a minute!
**Helper 1** | What was that?

**Helper 2** Did someone speak?

**Audience Voice 1** I said, just a minute. I don't quite understand about this Time Vortex business.

**Helpers** Oh dear, it's one of those.

**Master** *(To the Helpers.)* Haven't you two explained? Haven't you told them about the Time Vortex? You pair of squashed bananas! *(To the audience voice.)* Now, what was it you wanted to know?

**Audience Voice 1** Well, I know that you're called the Master of the Time Vortex, but I don't understand about the golden key and....

**Master** Say no more. You see, it's quite simple, really.

**Helper 1** The Time Vortex is the place where time stands still....

**Helper 2** And when the golden key is used to open the Time Vortex box, everything that has ever happened in the history of the world is released from time....

**Helper 1** So, every Christmas the Master has to visit one family and let them into the secret of the Time Vortex....

**Helper 2** And their reward is that they can choose to see anything.

**Audience Voice 1** What do you mean, 'anything'?

**Helpers** Simply that... anything.

Look, you just sit back and see it all happen. Now, if these two lay-abouts will cut the cackle, we can proceed into the Thins' house and get on with the business in hand. Say the magic word.

AL-A-KA-ZOOM. INTO THE ROOM!

*(Lights flash. Loud noise. The Master and the Helpers enter the house.)*

**Audience Voice 1** Seems daft to me. I don't understand about the...

**Audience Voice 2** Oh keep quiet. It's all very simple.

**Audience Voice 3** Shut up, you two. We're here to watch the play.

**Audience Voice 1** Yes but I don't understand....

**Stage Manager** *(Entering.)* Put a sock in it, will you? We'd like to get on with the story, if you don't mind. Come on, you actors. Next scene, if you please! Chop! Chop! *(He exits.)*

## Scene V

*Inside the Thins' living room. Tom creeps in through one door, and Jerry enters through a second door. They back towards each other and collide.*

| | |
|---|---|
| **Jerry** | Gosh, you scared me stiff! |
| **Tom** | I thought you were a ghost! |
| **Jerry** | Switch your torch on. |
| **Tom** | It's only three o'clock. Mum will kill us if we wake her. |
| | *(A tapping noise is heard.)* |
| **Jerry** | What's that noise? |
| **Susan** | *(Entering slowly.)* Where are the presents? |
| **Jerry and Tom** | You scared us! Creeping in like a burglar! |
| **Susan** | Has Santa Claus been yet? |
| **Jerry** | Santa Claus! Nonsense! |
| **Tom** | No, you two, don't start *that* argument again. I can't see any presents... |
| | *(A loud noise.)* |
| **Jerry** | Crumbs! |

**Tom** What was that?

**Susan** It's Santa Claus.

*(Enter Master, and two Helpers.)*

**Jerry** It can't be!

**Susan** It is! It's Santa Claus!

**Master** Wrong, my dear. Permit me to introduce myself. I am the Master of the Time Vortex.

**Helpers** And we are his Helpers.

**Master** I'm so glad that you're up and ready for my Magic Christmas Show.

**Jerry** What's that when it's around?

**Susan** So you're not Santa Claus?

**Master** No, I'm not. But I do have something that even Santa doesn't have. I have the golden key, and with it I can open the Time Vortex box.

**Helpers** And then you can all see the Magic Christmas Show.

**Master** Hurry up, quick, you choose first.

**Susan** Me? Choose? Choose what?

**Helper 1** Whatever it is in the world...

**Helper 2** ...that you'd most like to see.

**Susan** Well... well, I like reading stories about witches. So, I'd like to see... witches.

**Master** No problem. Witches without delay. I just unlock the box and *voilà*!

*(The Master turns the golden key in a large box marked 'TIME VORTEX'. Lights flash. Loud noise. Three Witches appear and circle around a cauldron in a 'spells' dance.)*

# Scene VI

*The Witches come to a standstill from dancing around the cauldron.*

**Witches** Hubble, bubble, at the double
cooking pot stir up some trouble.

**Witch 1** Into our pot there now must go
Leg of lamb and green frog's toe.

**Witch 2** Old man's socks and dirty jeans,
a rotten egg and cold baked beans.

**Witch 3** One dead fly and a wild wasp's sting,
the eye of a sheep and the heart of a king.

**Witches** *(Circling.)* Hubble, bubble, at the double
cooking pot stir up some trouble.

**Witch 1** A stolen jewel, and mouldy salt,

| | |
|---|---|
| | and for good flavour a jar of malt. |
| **Witch 2** | Wing of bird, and head of mouse, |
| | Screams and howls from a haunted house. |
| **Witch 3** | And don't forget the pint of blood, |
| | or the sardine tin, and the clod of mud. |
| **Witches** | *(Circling.)* Hubble, bubble, at the double |
| | cooking pot stir up some trouble. |
| **Witch 1** | Listen! Footsteps in the night! |
| **Witch 2** | Hark! Footsteps in the pale moonlight! |
| **Witch 3** | By the tree of the rotten plums something wicked this way comes! |
| | *(Wizard enters.)* |
| **Witches** | *(Bowing.)* Master, we obey your every wish. |
| | Would you like to sip our tasty dish? |
| **Wizard** | *(Tasting the soup from the cauldron.)* Um, that's good. Um, oh yes! |
| | Now my beauties, is all quite ready? |
| | It's getting past my beddy-weddy! |
| | That smells so horrid, bad and foul. |
| | Did you add the lion's growl? |
| | And surely you have not forgot |
| | The squealing rat for your cooking pot? |
| | *(Wizard produces a rat, and drops it into the cauldron. The Witches cackle loudly.)* |
| **Witch 1** | In it goes. Stir it well. |
| **Witch 2** | Now's the time to cast our spell. |
| **Witch 3** | ABRACADABRA doo dum dake |
| | ABRACADABRA doo dum doors |
| | Turn into a slippery snake |
| | Boys who don't believe in Santa Claus! |
| **Jerry** | *(Coming forward.)* Me... you don't mean me? Am I going to be turned into a slippery snake? |
| **Witch 1** | Oh drat and rat! The spell's not worked! |
| **Witch 2** | We had the same trouble last year! |
| **Witch 3** | What did we forget for the cauldron? What? |
| **Wizard** | Tut, tut, tut. The dog's tail, ladies? *(He holds it up.)* |
| | Well, there you are my pretty things |
| | Your rotten planning failure brings. |
| | Last year you left out ear of hog |
| | And this time forgot the tail of dog! |
| | YAAAAAAAAAAAH! |
| | *(The Wizard thumbs his nose at the Witches. They chase him from the stage. Loud shrieks and cackles.)* |

**Jerry** Wow!

**Tom** I really thought that you were about to be turned into a snake.

**Master** Well, children, how did you enjoy that little item from my Magic Christmas Show? I told you that the Vortex Box held some very interesting things indeed.

**Helper 1** You choose now, Tom.

**Helper 2** What do you want to see? What's your choice?

**Tom** Well... well... what about Red Indians?

**Master** Your wish is my command. I just turn the golden key and *voilà!*

# Scene VII

*Red Indians enter to a beating drum. A totem pole is placed in the centre of the stage. The Red Indians perform a dance around the totem pole. Chief Crazy Horse takes his place on a chair at the edge of the stage.*

**Indians** Chief Crazy Horse! Chief Crazy Horse!

**Indian 1** The most powerful chief of the Indian nation.

**Indian 2** The bravest Indian in all our lands.

**Indian 3** The fastest runner across the prairie.

**Indian 4** The great hunter of wild buffalo.

**Indian 5** The Indian chief feared by all the palefaces.

**Indians** Chief Crazy Horse! Chief Crazy Horse! The bravest Indian chief, of course!

*(Red Feet enters.)*

**Crazy Horse** Red Feet, come and stand close. Tell us one of your stories.

**Indians** Red Feet, the teller of stories.

**Red Feet** I have, for your delight tonight, a tale of bravery.

**Indians** Ah!

**Red Feet** Bravery and death.

**Indians** Ah!

**Red Feet** Bravery and death and victory over the palefaces.

**Indians** Ah! Ah!

**Crazy Horse** Palefaces! Enemies! Tell us your story on this night of wild winds and snow.

**Red Feet** The night was black. The stars were bright. The moon stared down. Moon's face a light.

**Indians** Pow!

**Red Feet** The Indian braves met down at the river
And feasted on corn and buffalo liver.

**Indians** Pow!

**Red Feet** Then up stood Crazy Horse ready to fight
The hated palefaces with all his might.

**Indians** Pow! Pow!

**Red Feet** The Indians rode on their horses fast
Until they reached the fort at last.

**Indians** Pow!

**Red Feet** They loosed their arrows tipped with flame
And with whoops and cries joined in the game.
With tomahawks they scalped a few
And stabbed and knifed the uniforms blue.
But the paleface spoke with cannon and gun
And killed the Indians... all but one.

**Indians** Who? Tell us who?

**Red Feet** Chief Crazy Horse escaped that place
Where his braves met the hated paleface.
He rode away to the lake and the hill
Where the snow lies deep and the air is still.

**Indians** Crazy Horse! Crazy Horse!

**Indian 1** The greatest Indian chief!

**Indian 2** Yellowhair Custer! Me scalp him!

**Indian 3** Burn the fort! Burn the fort!

**Indian 4** Revenge! Let us revenge our Indian braves!

**Indian 5** Chief Crazy Horse... lead us to victory!

**Indians** Pow! Pow! Pow!

*(The Indians move around the stage. Tom thinks that they are stalking him. He hastily moves away and hides behind the Master. After circling the totem pole the Red Indians exit with whoops and shouts.)*

**Tom** Have they gone?

**Jerry** I think so.

**Susan** What a noise.

**Tom** They *must* have woken up Mum.

**Master** Not at all.

**Tom** I thought they were after me!

**Master** No, no, no. It was *your* Christmas choice.

**Helper 1** Remember, no one knows anything about the Time Vortex except the people witnessing the events.

**Helper 2** And it's your choice now, Jerry Thin. What do you want to see?

**Jerry** Well... I bet that you can't conjure up pirates.

**Helpers** Pirates? No problem.

**Master** Easy. Let's turn the golden key and... *voilà*!

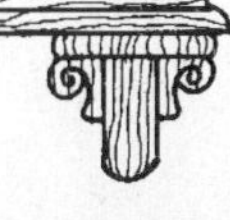

# Scene VIII

*The Pirates enter. They form a semi-circle, sit down and drink from bottles of rum.*

| | |
|---|---|
| **Pirates** | Fifteen men on a dead man's chest,<br>Yo-ho-ho and a bottle of rum.<br>Long John's wearing a dirty vest<br>Yo-ho-ho and a bottle or rum. |
| **Long Johns** | What's that? Who's wearing a dirty vest? |
| **Pirates** | You are, Long Johns! |
| **Long Johns** | Well, never mind about that. Where's the map? |
| **Pirates** | Map? What map? |
| **Long Johns** | The treasure map, you swabs. Where is it? |
| **Dirty-Hands George** | You had it last, Long Johns. |
| **Black Doggy** | That's right. You had it, Long Johns. |
| **Long Johns** | Okay, okay. Let's have a little search for it. *(He makes a great fuss while searching through his clothing.)* |
| **Billy the Rum** | You've lost it. |
| **Black Doggy** | He's lost it. |
| **Pirates** | What an idiot! He's lost his treasure map! |
| **Long Johns** | Wait, me hearties, wait. I reckon that young swab has stolen it from off my person. |
| **Pirates** | Who? What young swab? |

**Long Johns** Why, young Hawkins.

**Dirty-Hands**

**George** Hawkins?

**Pirates** Hawkins! Where is he?

**Long Johns** He's double-crossed us, my hearties. He must have stolen the map while I slept last night.

**Black Doggy** Then we must find him, search him out.

**Pirates** Hawkins, the young swab! Find him!

**Long Johns** Yellowdog Pete, come here. Off you trot now and find master Hawkins. Bring him here and we'll...

**Pirates** ...cut his throat!

**Long Johns** Take Billy the Rum and find the little...

**Pirates** ...traitor! Find him. Find the treasure map. Hawkins has it!

**Yellowdog Pete** Aye, aye, Long Johns.

**Billy the Rum** We'll find him, Long Johns.

*(They search around the stage, and then exit.)*

**Long Johns** Now, my hearties, my shipmates. What about a little song for old Long Johns while we wait for Yellowdog and Billy the Rum to return with the young swab Hawkins... and the treasure map. What about a song?

**Pirates** Aye, aye, Long Johns.

*(They sing. A couple of Pirates do a jig.)*

Fifteen men on a dead man's chest,

Yo-ho-ho and a bottle of rum.

Long John's wearing a dirty vest,

Yo-ho-ho and a bottle of rum.

Where will we find the treasure map?

Yo-ho-ho and a bottle of rum.

In Hawkins' sock or in his cap?

Yo-ho-ho and a bottle of rum.

**Long Johns** Quiet, lads. Sshhhh! Here come Yellowdog and Billy the Rum. Look, they're still searching....

*(Enter Yellowdog Pete and Billy the Rum. They slowly move around the stage. Eventually they come across Jerry who is watching from the side.)*

**Yellowdog Pete** Got you Hawkins.

**Billy the Rum** *(Grabbing Jerry.)* Hold him, Yellowdog. Don't let him go.

**Yellowdog Pete** Take him to Long Johns.

*(They drag Jerry over to confront Long Johns.)*

**Jerry** I'm not young Hawkins! I haven't got the treasure map!

**Long Johns** Silence!

| | |
|---|---|
| **Pirates** | Silence, Hawkins! |
| **Long Johns** | The treasure map, NOW! |
| **Pirates** | Hand it over. |
| **Long Johns** | No delay. The treasure map, if you please or we'll... |
| **Pirates** | ...cut your throat! |
| **Jerry** | I haven't got the map. I'm not Hawkins. My name is Jerry Thin. |
| **Long Johns** | And I suppose you've got a brother called Tom! |
| **Pirates** | Tom and Jerry! *(They all roar with laughter.)* |
| **Jerry** | But I am not Hawkins, I'm not. It's the truth. |
| **Pirates** | Then cut his throat! Let's do it. |
| | *(The Pirates draw their knives. They close in on Jerry. Susan comes to the front of the stage.)* |
| **Susan** | Master! Do something! They're going to cut my brother's throat! |
| **Master** | This is an emergency. I'll have to turn the golden key in the Time Vortex box and.... |
| | *(Lights flash. Loud noise. The Pirates exit hurriedly.)* |
| **Tom** | Jerry, are you okay? |
| **Susan** | I thought that you'd had it that time. |
| **Jerry** | I'm all in one piece... just. |
| **Master** | You were very lucky. Somehow you got caught up in the Time Vortex. |
| **Helper 1** | The golden key must be returned to Santa Claus... |
| **Helper 2** | ...before six o'clock. |
| **Master** | So, no time to lose. Bye for now, children. I hope that you enjoyed my Magic Christmas Show. |
| **Children** | We certainly did. |
| **Helpers** | Back to the North Pole, Master. Come along. Bye, bye everyone. |
| | *(Lights flash. Loud noise. Master and Helpers exit.)* |
| **Tom** | What an evening! |
| **Jerry** | There were Red Indians... |
| **Susan** | ...and three witches and a wizard... |
| **Tom** | ...and pirates. |
| **Jerry** | Time we were back in bed, I reckon. |
| **Susan** | Just a second. Listen. |
| | *(Sound of sleigh bells.)* |
| **Tom** | It's old Santa Claus. He's nearly here! |
| **Jerry** | Then let's get back to bed... quickly! I don't fancy meeting *him* after all that's happened tonight. |
| | *(The children exit. The sound of sleigh bells increases in volume.)* |

# Scene IX

*The Star Dancers enter. They perform a dance to a piece of Christmas music. By the end of the dance, the dancers have arranged themselves at the back of the Thin's living room. Enter Santa Claus and Clerks.*

| | |
|---|---|
| **Santa Claus** | All quiet? Yes, seems quiet anyway. Put the presents out. Quickly, now. Hurry, hurry. |
| **Clerk 1** | *(Taking presents from a sack.)* That's all we've doing all night long... hurrying. |
| **Clerk 2** | *(Checking a clip-board.)* This is the Thins' house, and the children have asked for.... |
| **Santa Claus** | What was that name? |
| **Clerk 2** | The Thins... wait a minute. Wasn't that the family due to be visited by the Master of the Time Vortex? |
| **Clerk 1** | Yes, it was. He must have been... and gone. |
| **Santa Claus** | I only hope he managed to return the golden key in time. Now, how are we doing? |
| **Clerk 1** | Finished. All the presents are set out. |
| **Santa Claus** | Right, then. Off we go. Are the reindeer well filled with lead-free petrol? |
| **Clerks** | Of course. |
| | *(Santa Claus and Clerks exit. The Star Dancers perform a brief dance and they too exit.)* |

# Scene X

*Next morning – Christmas Day. Mrs Thin enters and looks at the presents, then goes to the door and shouts...*

| | |
|---|---|
| **Mrs Thin** | Children! Tom! Jerry! Susan! It's Christmas Day, and it's nearly nine o'clock. What's the matter with you? You're usually up hours before this on Christmas Day! *(Mrs Thin exits.)* |
| **Tom** | *(Entering... He is wearing pyjamas.)* Nine o'clock! I suppose that's because I was up half the night. |
| **Jerry** | *(Entering.)* Hey, look at those presents! Not bad, not bad. |
| **Susan** | *(Entering)* I'm tired. I had the strangest dream last night. I dreamed that I saw witches and a wizard.... |
| **Tom and Jerry** | Sssssssh! That's a secret, stupid! |
| **Susan** | That's right, it *wasn't* a dream! Just look at all those presents. |
| | *(The children begin to open various parcels.)* |
| **Jerry** | I've got a ray gun. |
| **Tom** | Look at this. It's a stamp album, and three packets of stamps. |

**Susan** I've got a wooden recorder.

**Jerry** Well, I'll be blowed.

**Tom and Susan** What? What is it?

**Jerry** Look what I've found.

**Tom and Susan** What is it? We're busy!

**Jerry** It's... it's a golden snake.

**Tom** *(Examining the snake.)* It's the snake that the Master of the Time Vortex was wearing.

**Susan** So it is. He had it around his neck. It must have dropped off the chain... and it's fallen here.

**Jerry** Then it's ours.

**Tom** Well, he won't come back for it now, of that I'm certain.

**Susan** He's at the North Pole now, anyway.

**Jerry** Then this is the best Christmas present of all. The Master's golden snake! It will always be a reminder of the night we saw his Magic Christmas Show. And to think that I complained about it being a boring, quiet Christmas when nothing was going to happen.

**Tom** Just shows how wrong you were. It's been a great Christmas already and it's only just begun. And it's all thanks to....

**Children** The Master of the Time Vortex and his Magic Christmas Show!

**Jerry** Come on, let's open these other presents.

*(The children open their other presents. Christmas music is heard. Mrs Thin enters, quietly. She beckons the rest of the cast on stage. Gradually they assemble behind the children, who do not see them arrive. The children are engrossed in their presents and parcels. When the cast has assembled the music ceases.)*

**Cast** Happy Christmas Tom, Jerry and Susan!

**Children** *(Turning.)* What? Well....

**Cast** Happy Christmas Tom, Jerry and Susan.

**Master and Santa Claus** *(Stepping forward.)* Happy Christmas to you all. What about our Christmas song?

*(The cast sing a Christmas song.)*

Wes Magee

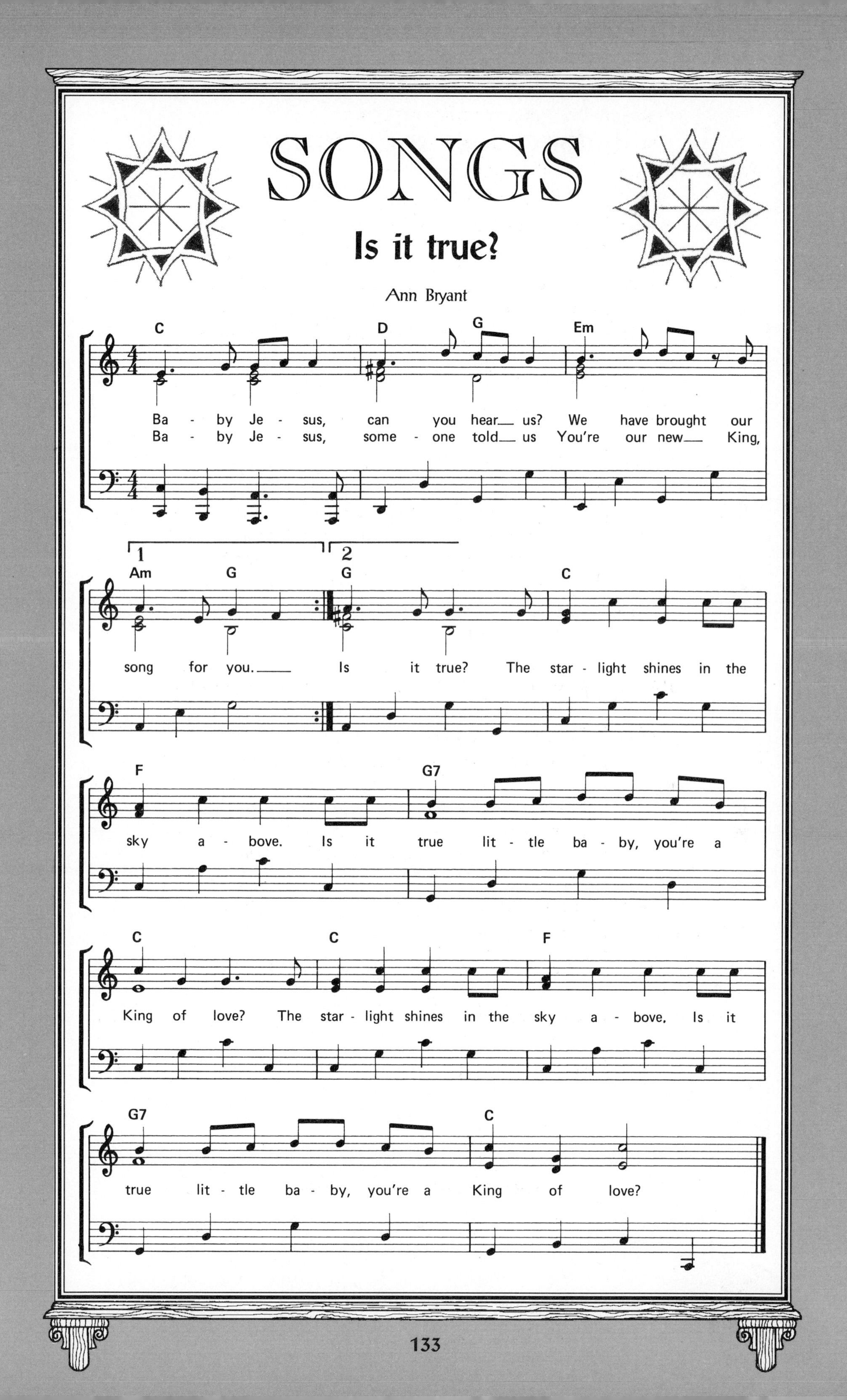
SONGS
Is it true?
Ann Bryant
C D G Em
Ba - by Je - sus, can you hear__ us? We have brought our
Ba - by Je - sus, some - one told__ us You're our new__ King,
1 2
Am G G C
song for you.___ Is it true? The star - light shines in the
F G7
sky a - bove. Is it true lit - tle ba - by, you're a
C C F
King of love? The star - light shines in the sky a - bove. Is it
G7 C
true lit - tle ba - by, you're a King of love?
133

# I danced in the morning

Music by Sydney Carter and words adapted by Ann Bryant

2. I danced in the angels when they spread their wings,
And they lit up the sky to make everybody sing.
They flew down to tell the shepherds what to do,
A baby King, yes, yes it's true.

Chorus

3. I danced in the shepherds as they watched their sheep,
Although they were tired they just couldn't go to sleep.
They flew down to tell the shepherds what to do,
A baby King, yes, yes it's true.

Chorus

4. I danced in the animals, the cat, the mouse,
The goat and the cow that let Jesus share their house.
They lay down beside the baby, soft and new,
A baby King, yes, yes it's true.

Chorus

5. I danced in the Kings and Queens who travelled far,
They followed the light of the great big silver star.
They came to the stable and their happiness grew,
A baby King, yes, yes it's true.

Chorus

6. I danced in the children as they smiled and sang,
All over the world bells of glory glory rang.
The children danced and the world danced too,
A baby King, yes, yes it's true.

Chorus

# Angel song

Ann Bryant

# Animal song

Ann Bryant

2. The sheep looked at the baby and said, 'Baa baa baa'.
3. The pigs looked at the baby and said, 'Oink oink oink'.
4. The dogs looked at the baby and said, 'Woof woof woof'.
5. The cats looked at the baby and said, 'Miaow miaow miaow'.
6. The mice looked at the baby and said, 'Squeak squeak squeak'.

# Kings' and queens' song

2. Kings Kings Kings, from the East! Etc.

Christmas bells
David Moses
Group 1
Group 2
D
Em
1.Christ - mas bells go ding ding ding
2. Rein deers' hoooves go clip clip clip
3. San - ta's laugh - ing ha ha ha
4. Op en the pre - sents ooh ooh ooh
Christ mas bells go
Rein - deers' hooves go
San - ta's laugh - ing
Op - en the pre - sents
D
Em
A7
Ding ding ding Sing for Christ - mas
Clip clip clip Sing for Christ - mas
Ha ha ha Sing for Christ - mas
ooh ooh ooh Sing for Christ - mas
dong dong dong Dong dong dong Sing for Christ - mas
clop clop clop Clop clop clop Sing for Christ - mas
ho ho ho Ho ho ho Sing for Christ - mas
ah ah ah Ah ah ah Sing for Christ - mas
D
D
Em
D
Em
D
Em
ev - ery - one. Ding ding Ding ding Ding ding
ev - ery - one. Clip clip Clip clip Clip clip
ev - ery - one. Ha ha Ha ha Ha ha
ev - ery - one. Ooh ooh Ooh ooh Ooh ooh
ev- ery-one. Dong dong Dong dong Dong dong
ev- ery-one. Clop clop Clop clop Clop clop
ev- ery-one. Ho ho Ho ho Ho ho
ev- ery-one. Ah ah Ah ah Ah ah
D
Em
A7
D
Ding ding Sing for Christ - mas ev - ery - one.
Clip clip Sing for Christ - mas ev - ery - one.
Ha ha Sing for Christ - mas ev - ery - one.
Ooh ooh Sing for Christ - mas ev - ery - one.
Dong dong Sing for Christ - mas ev - ery - one.
Clop clop Sing for Christ - mas ev - ery - one.
Ho ho Sing for Christ - mas ev - ery - one.
Ah ah Sing for Christ - mas ev - ery - one.

# Greedylumps' exercise song

Ann Bryant

F
2. Jen - ny Gree-dy-lump jump-ing out and in. What a pi - ty it
Two-tone woodblock - - - staccato throughout
C7
does-n't make her thin. Out and in from morn-ing un-til night,
F
C7
F
F
Jen - ny Gree-dy-lump, What a fun-ny sight! 3. Jim - my Gree-dy-lump,
claves throughout
etc.
C7
run-ning on the spot. Don't you love that Gree-dy-lump trot. Run run run from
staccato . . . .
F
C7
F
morn-ing un-til night. Jim - my Gree-dy-lump, What a fun-ny sight!

# Grumpydumps' work piece

Ann Bryant

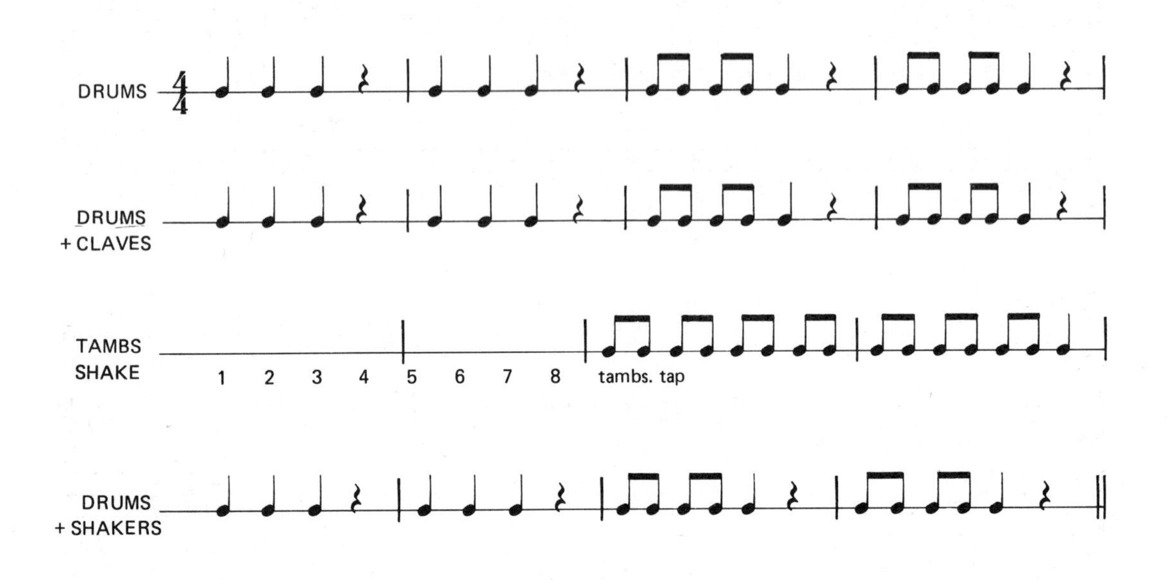


# Lazyslumps' song

Ann Bryant

2. Nice to have some friends for tea,
There's nothing we like more.
Nothing we like more,
Nothing we like more.
Nice to have some friends for tea,
There's nothing we like more.
The trouble is we're all so lazy,
No one wants to pour!

3. Nice to have some friends to stay,
There's nothing we like more.
Nothing we like more,
Nothing we like more.
Nice to have some friends to stay,
Thre's nothing we like more.
The trouble is we're all so lazy,
No one opens the door!

# Jesus was a baby in Bethlehem

David Moses

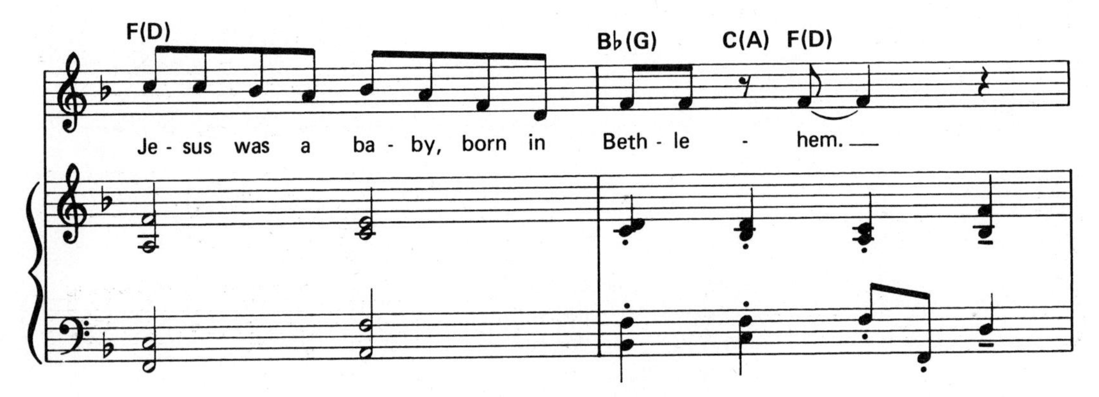


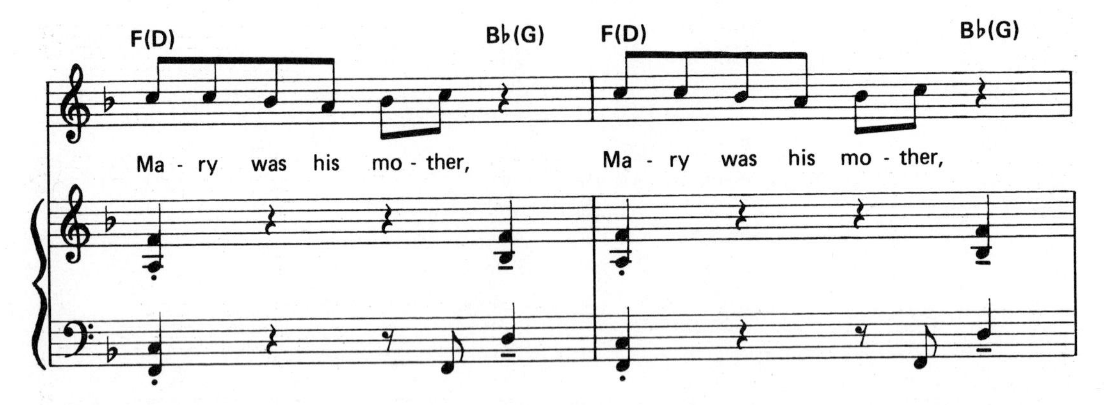

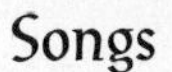

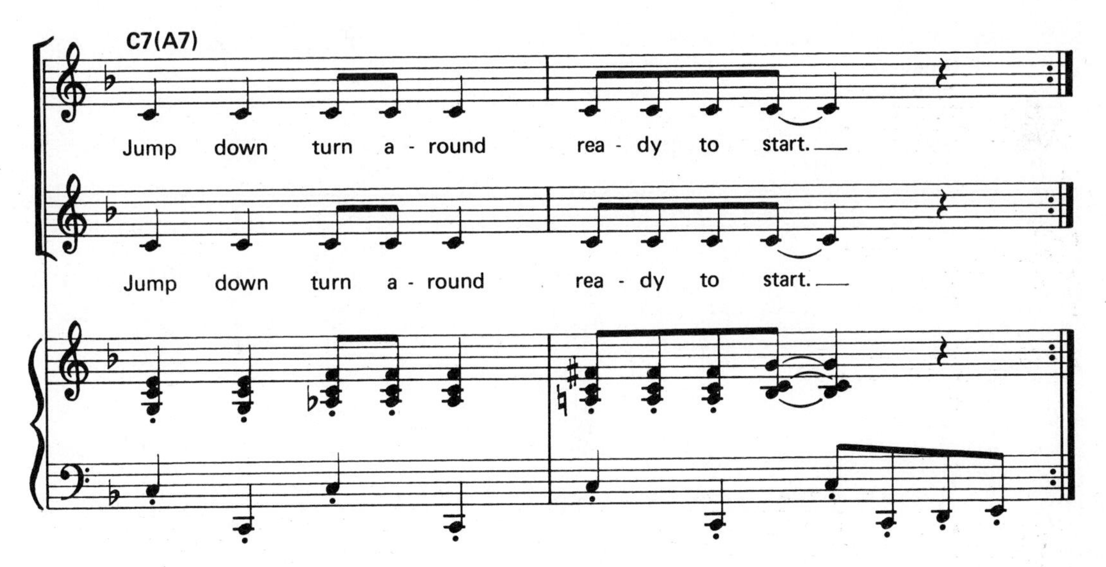


2. Joseph was his daddy,
Joseph was his daddy,
Joseph was his daddy in Bethlehem.
Shepherds came to see him,
Shepherds came to see him,
Shepherds came to see him in Bethlehem.

Chorus

3. Angels singing 'Glory',
Angels singing 'Glory',
Angels singing 'Glory' in Bethlehem.
Telling out the story,
Telling out the story,
Telling out the story of Bethlehem.

Chorus

# Sleep little baby

Music by Peter Morrell and words by Elizabeth Chapman

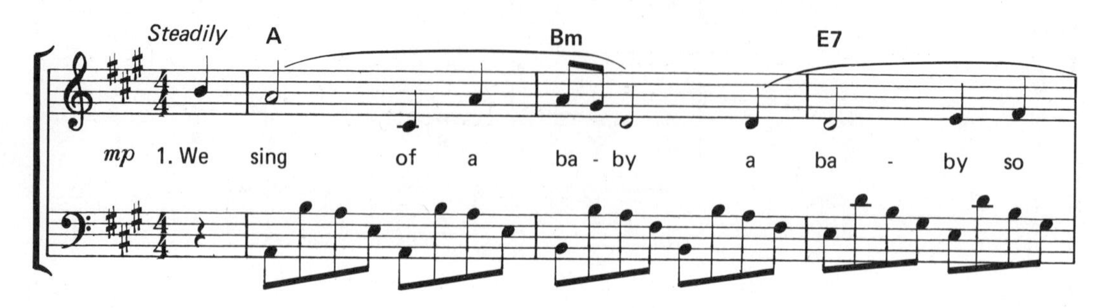


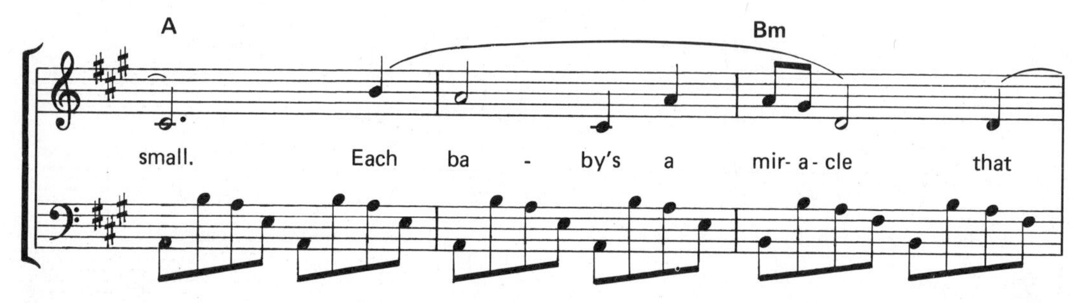


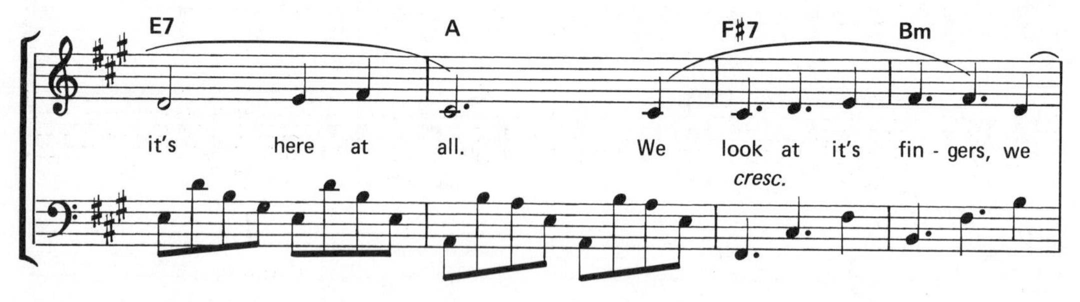


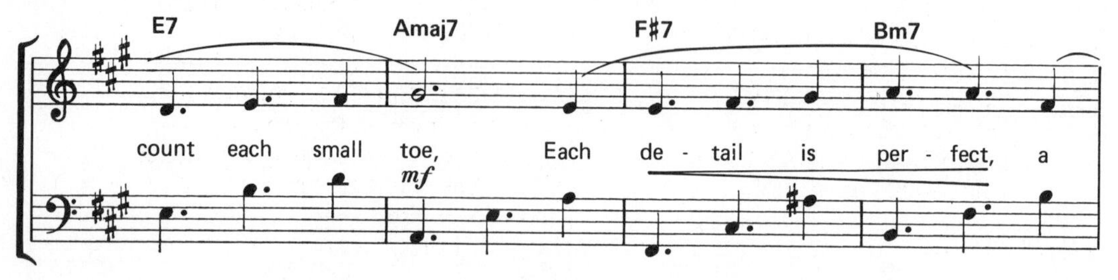

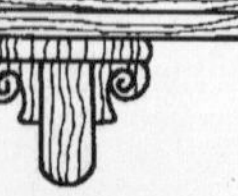

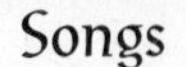

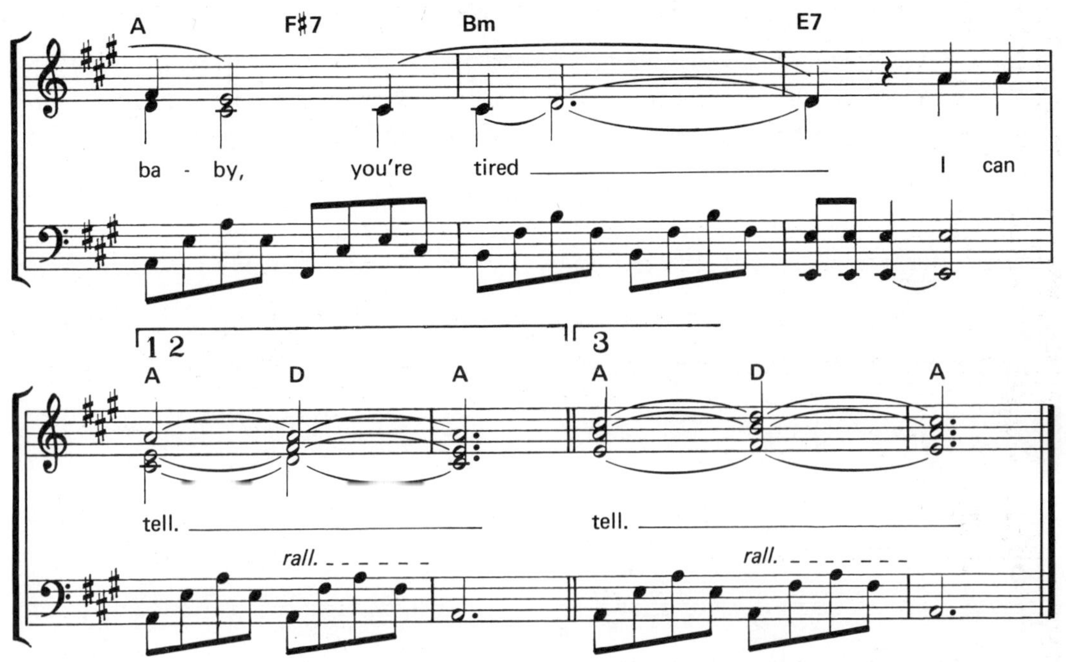


2. You cry, we come running
You smile and we glow,
You make us remember
A birth long ago.
He lived in no palace,
No wrappings of silk,
Like you He just lay there
And drank only milk.

Chorus

3. Yet still we remember
Through thousands of years
A baby, a promise
Of help through our fears.
Each baby's so special,
Unique in its way,
Like He who we're praising
On this Christmas Day.

Chorus

# Merry Christmas

Gillian Parker

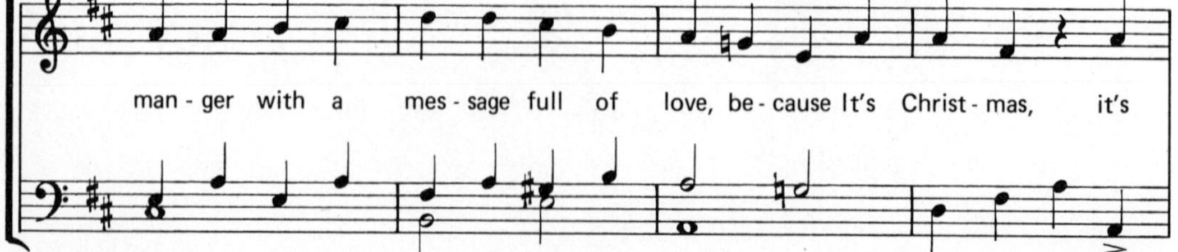

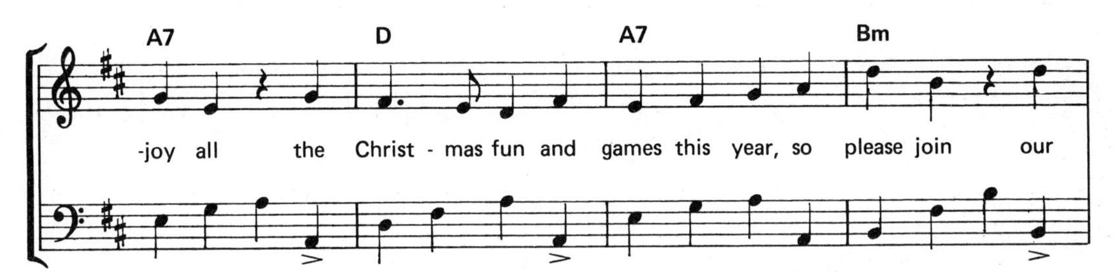

2. We hope that you will all enjoy our Christmas play this year,
It tells a story full of hope, a message of good cheer.
Mary on a donkey, an inn at Bethlehem,
A stable with an ox and ass and gifts from three wide men, because...

Chorus

3. On your way back home tonight please listen for the sound
Of angel voices, Christmas loud ringing all around,
See the wondrous faces of people passing by,
Who stop and stare and marvel at the star up in the sky, because...

Chorus

# I wonder how it was

Traditional tune (The Ashgrove Song) and words adapted by Mike Fenton

2. Holy couple, so weary, at the end of
 their journey,
So sad to discover, no room at the inn.
So a straw-laden manger,
Was the bed for the little stranger,
Who was born our dear saviour,
To set the world free.

Chorus

3. Oh, I wish I'd been able to be in
 that stable,
To share in a new dawning when
 Jesus was born.
I would know of the beauty,
I would understand completely,
To behold the glad tidings,
When a new babe is born.

Chorus

4. Oh, what can I give Him, to show
 that I love Him,
As did shepherds and wise men
 when Jesus was born?
I can sing of the glory,
Of the beautiful story,
Which gives us such happiness,
Hope for mankind.

Chorus

5. From Advent to New Year,
 we'll be full of good cheer,
To celebrate Christmas the way it
 should be.
In these times when He needs us,
We'll remember the baby Jesus,
And go where He leads us,
That we might be free.

Chorus

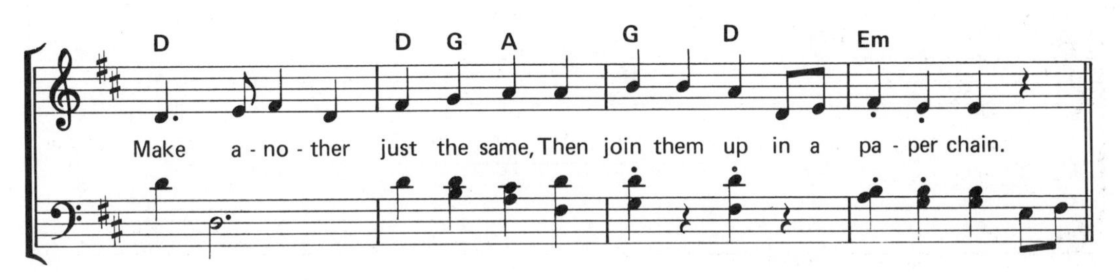


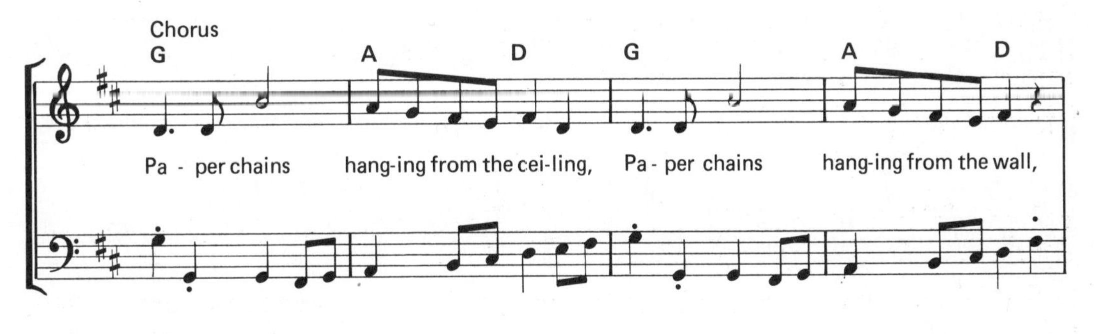


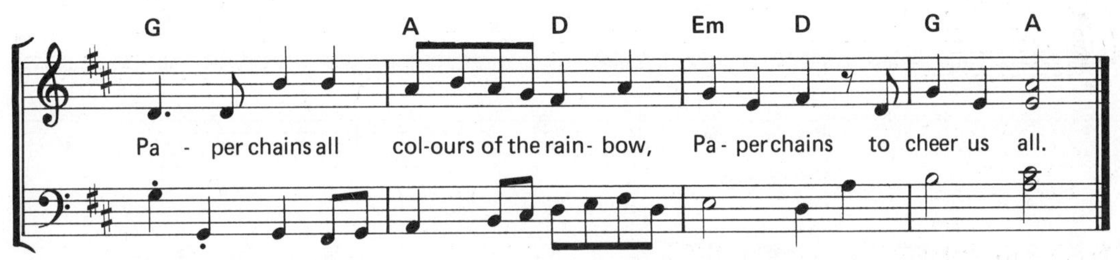


2. Cut a square out,
Cut a pair out,
Join the two with
Sticky glue to
Make a star as bright as flame,
Then hang it up with the paper chains.

Chorus

3. Make a tree shape
Or a free shape,
Have a go at
Fluffy snow or
Paint some frost on the window pane,
Sprinkle glitter on the paper chains.

Chorus

4. Coloured lights all
Twinkle brightly,
Shiny bangles,
Pretty candles,
Sweets and present, songs and games,
Tinsel streamers and paper chains.

Chorus

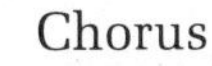

# Do you believe in Father Christmas?

Debbie Campbell

# GAMES

## Christmas scavenge

**Players**
Any number.

**How to play**
Ask the children to collect as many of the following items as they can during the Christmas holidays or over a weekend.

- a Christmas stocking (3);
- an unpulled Christmas cracker (5);
- a Christmas napkin (7);
- a piece of holly (5);
- a piece of Christmas tree (3);
- a label from a Christmas pudding (5);
- a photograph of the Christmas dinner (10);
- Christmas wrapping paper with reindeer on (5);
- a Christmas carrier bag (5);
- a Christmas stamp (3);
- an unused Christmas card (3);
- a ticket from a panto or Christmas show (8);
- a programme from the same show (8);
- a card from Father Christmas (12);
- a photograph of Father Christmas (8);
- an empty mince pie box (5);
- a painting of Rudolph (12);
- a home-made Christmas decoration (8);
- a home-made Christmas cracker (10);
- the hat from inside a cracker (3);
- a toy from inside a cracker (3);
- the explosive strip from a cracker (3);
- a thank you letter to Father Christmas (5);
- a Christmas painting (8);

Each item has a score against it with the more unusual items having a higher score. The winner is the child who has the most points.

The children should be encouraged to use their initiative to collect these items; for example, they need not necessarily go to see the pantomime, they could simply ask at the theatre for a used ticket!

# Guess the present

**Players**

Any number.

**How to play**

Think of a Christmas present or ask one of the children to think of one. The children must then take it in turns to ask questions to try and find out what the present is. The person who thought of the present is only allowed to answer yes or no to the questions, which should be limited to 20.

When playing this game with children it may be better to divide the class up into teams so that several games can be played at the same time. If this was carried out in the school hall the groups would be far enough away from each other not to disturb each other. It would mean that more children would have more turns at answering the questions.

# Christmas riddles

**Players**

Any number.

**How to play**

Prepare two different sets of cards so that one set has some Christmas riddles on them and the second has the answers to the riddles (see pages 30 and 31 for possible riddles). Divide the children into two groups and give each child in each group a riddle card and each child in the other group an answer card.

On the word 'go' each child has to find her partner by matching the riddles to the answers.

The children have great fun making up their own Christmas riddles and trying them out on each other.

# Christmas tree words

**Players**
Two or more.

**What you need**
Pencils, score paper.

**How to play**
Ask the children to think of homophones such as 'pear' and 'pair'. One child should then put both words in a sentence, but replace the homophones with the words 'Christmas tree'.

Other children must then try to guess the homophones by asking one question each. The child has to respond to each question by using one of the homophones in a sentence, but of course replacing it with 'Christmas tree', for example: The Christmas tree fell off the tree on to a Christmas tree of dogs (pear, pair).

Question: Can you eat your Christmas tree?

Answer: A Christmas tree of tights would not taste very good.

The idea is to put the other children off the track as much as possible and yet each answer will provide the other players with further contexts for the homophones.

It would be useful for all the players to have access to some paper so that they can write down their thoughts.

Each child should be given the chance to think of homophones and points can be awarded to the child who manages to guess the words. If the words are not guessed correctly the player who thought up the words can score the points. The winner is the player with the most points at the end.

# Christmas sounds

**Players**

Any number.

**How to play**

The object of this game is for the children to recognise and respond to different sounds in the following way:

- jingle bells – Father Christmas is coming! All the children should pretend to be asleep;
- triangle – angels spread their wings;
- cymbals – shepherds hide their eyes from the angel's light;
- tambourine – put hands on shoulders ready to dance;
- Indian bells – point up high, to star over stable;
- drums – the Kings are coming all the children put should put their hands on their heads to form crowns.

Play each instrument out of sight of the children and as soon as the instrument is played the children must react to the sound in the way specified. The last child to respond correctly, or any child who makes the wrong response is out. Continue like this until only one winner remains.

With very young children you will need to have a few practices until they know the correct response easily. You could also place symbols for each instrument together with its response on the wall to help them initially.

The children can also think of further ideas to extend and adapt this game or a child can be allowed to make the different sounds. How fast can the game be played?

# Christmas mimes

**Players**

Two teams of four.

**How to play**

Write out a number of Christmas words on to the cards. (You should bear in mind that these words will have to be mimed by the children.) For example:

- Christmas tree;
- angel;
- cracker;
- Father Christmas;
- reindeer;
- shepherd;
- holly;
- present;
- bell;
- turkey.

To add an element of competition have the winners from each gamo play each other ending up with a grand final where the words are made a lot more difficult.

# Christmas pictures

**Players**

Any number.

**How to play**

Depending on the length of game you want to play, choose anything from 4 to 20 Christmas cards. The pictures on each one should be as 'busy' as possible and from each one you should pick out an object which does not appear on any of the other cards. Number each card and stick the pictures around the area.

Having done this you should draw up a 'master' score sheet showing each player's name along the top and listing each key object and card number down the left-hand side.

You should then whisper different key objects to each child who must then find it on a picture. Once they have located the object on a card they should return to you and tell you the card number. You can mark this off on the master score card and tell them another object to find.

The children should not confer during this game and the player who finds all the items first, is the winner.

Ann Bryant

# Animals in the stable

**Players**
The whole class.

**How to play**
Make five 'leader' cards showing a donkey, sheep, cow, dog and cat. Use the templates below to make them and ensure that each leader card has the word 'leader' clearly shown. Then make five further cards for each animal, but without the word 'leader' on them. The object of this is that there should be enough cards for each child and therefore the numbers should be adjusted accordingly. Mix up all the cards and spread them face down and ask each child to pick a card.

The children who pick out the leader cards will be the team leaders and should stand in the middle of the room. The rest of the children can then spread out around the room. These children must not disclose to anyone else what animal card they picked. They should then start to make the noise of their animals as loudly as they can. When the leaders hear the noise of their animals they must go to that child and bring her into the middle. Once this happens she should stop making her noise.

When all the children have been found by their leaders each team must stand in line. The first team to find all its animals and stand in a line is the winner. But, having finished the game all the team members must show their cards to the team leader to prove they have been correctly picked. If someone is not in the correct team this team cannot win the game. Emphasise that the cards must not be shown until the game is finished.

Leader
Leader
Leader
Leader

# Picturise it!

**Players**

Any number.

**How to play**

Give each child a piece of squared paper and ask them to divide it into nine squares. They should then write in the left-hand corner of each square each letter of the word 'Christmas'. In each box the children must draw a picture of something connected with Christmas and beginning with the given letter. Award one point for each connection with Christmas and one point for each correct letter connection. This will give a possible top score of 18. Bonus points may be given for particularly well drawn or imaginative pictures.

The child who ends up with the most points is the winner.

# Father Christmas's treasure

**Players**

Any number.

**How to play**

Choose one child to be Father Christmas and blindfold him and sit him on a chair in the middle of the area. Underneath the chair you can place a number of different objects – make sure that most of them will make a noise when disturbed, for example a box containing marbles, presents wrapped in noisy, crinkly paper and so on. The rest of the children must then take it in turns to creep up to Father Christmas and try to steal a present.

Father Christmas should try to guard his presents and when he hears a movement must point in the direction of the sound. If he points at the thief then she has to return to her place. However, if this leads to argument use a torch to point with and then it will be easy to see if the thief is caught.

To add excitement and if this is played outside, Father Christmas can use a water pistol and shoot at the thieves with this. The water pistol will also help to prevent children pointing randomly as you can add the proviso that once the water pistol is empty the presents will be unprotected.

# Musical Christmas trees

**Players**

Any number.

**How to play**

Cut out a number of Christmas tree shapes from newspaper so that there are enough trees for the number of children playing the game. Ask the children to run around the room in different directions in time to some music. When the music stops each child must stand on a paper tree. Before the music stops you should take a tree or two away. The children are not in competition with each other, but, must help each other get on to the smaller and smaller number of Christmas trees. They must find imaginative ways of keeping everybody on the paper, such as, piggy backs.

# Fill Santa's sack

**Players**
Four or more.

**How to play**
The children should play with partners. One child in each pair should stand with his back to the wall holding open a sack while the other child should be on her hands and knees and blindfolded. On the word go she has to crawl towards the other end of the room, pick up an object from a pile and crawl back and put it in the sack. She should do this six times until all six presents are in the sack. However, she must only carry one present at a time and the child holding the sack must touch the wall with either his hand or foot at all times. He can shout encouragement or instructions whenever necessary, but he cannot physically help.

Leave the presents in a jumble at the other end of the room so that all the pairs have to take from the same place or you can leave them so that each pair has their own pile to take from.

To make this more difficult put obstacles in the path of the blindfolded children so that they have to get over, under or through them. Also you can make the objects awkward to carry, to make the game even more difficult. If the child drops the present she must go back to the beginning and start again with another present and the present that was dropped goes back into the pile. The winning team is the one that finishes first.

If catering for a large class then play this game as a relay race with each child collecting one present each, and staging heats and a final.

# Christmas cracker

**Players**
Any number.

**How to play**
Ask all the players to sit on chairs in a circle with one child in the middle of the circle. This child is the Christmas Elf, and he should shut his eyes and say:

Christmas Cracker
Where are you?
I need you back by
Half past two.

While the rhyme is being said the rest of the children should pass around a cracker behind their backs. When the rhyme is finished the Christmas Elf should open his eyes and point to who he thinks is hiding the cracker. If he guesses correctly, the child with the cracker becomes the Christmas Elf and the game continues.

# On the first day of Christmas

**Players**
Small group or a whole class.

**How to play**
Ask the children to sit in a circle. One child begins by saying, 'On the first day of Christmas, Father Christmas gave to me...' and names a present.

The game continues in progression, up to the twelfth day of Christmas, with each player repeating what has been said before and then adding his own present. However, if a mistake is made, the first child to raise his hand is allowed to begin the game again.

# Gift guesstimate

**Players**

Pairs.

**What you need**

A set of cards each showing a different gift item and its prices (these can be cut out from catalogues, magazines or newspapers); a set of cards each indicating a different amount of money; a calculator.

**How to play**

The cards should be placed face down in two piles between the two players. The players take it in turns to draw one card from each pile and quickly estimate how many of the gift items she can buy with the amount shown on the money card. The other player can challenge her opponent and the answers should be checked using the calculator. A point is scored for every correct estimate and can be recorded on a tally sheet.

The cards should then be replaced at the bottom of the piles. The winner is the player who has the most points at a given period of time, or who reaches a preset number of points first.

# Make the words

**Players**

Any number.

**How to play**

Give all the children a piece of paper and choose a Christmas phrase or name such as, 'Rudolph the red-nosed reindeer', and ask all the children to write it down. The game can then continue in one of two ways.

- Everyone makes up as many words as they can, using the letters in the phrase, in ten minutes. The winner is the child who makes up the most words.
- Take the first letter of the name or phrase and then everyone must think of as many words beginning with that letter as possible in two minutes. They can then take the next letter of the word and do the same until all the letters in the phrase or name have been used.

When a letter is repeated the children must think of new words which means that the children will really have to work hard to think of new words. The winner is the child who thinks of the most words.

# Grid words

**Players**

Any number.

**Materials**

Pencils, paper, dictionary, stop watch.

**How to play**

Give the children a word and ask them to write it in the middle of a piece of paper. Give the children five minutes to add as many words as possible to the original word. All the words must be connected in some way with the original word 'reindeer'; the children may come up with something resembling the following:

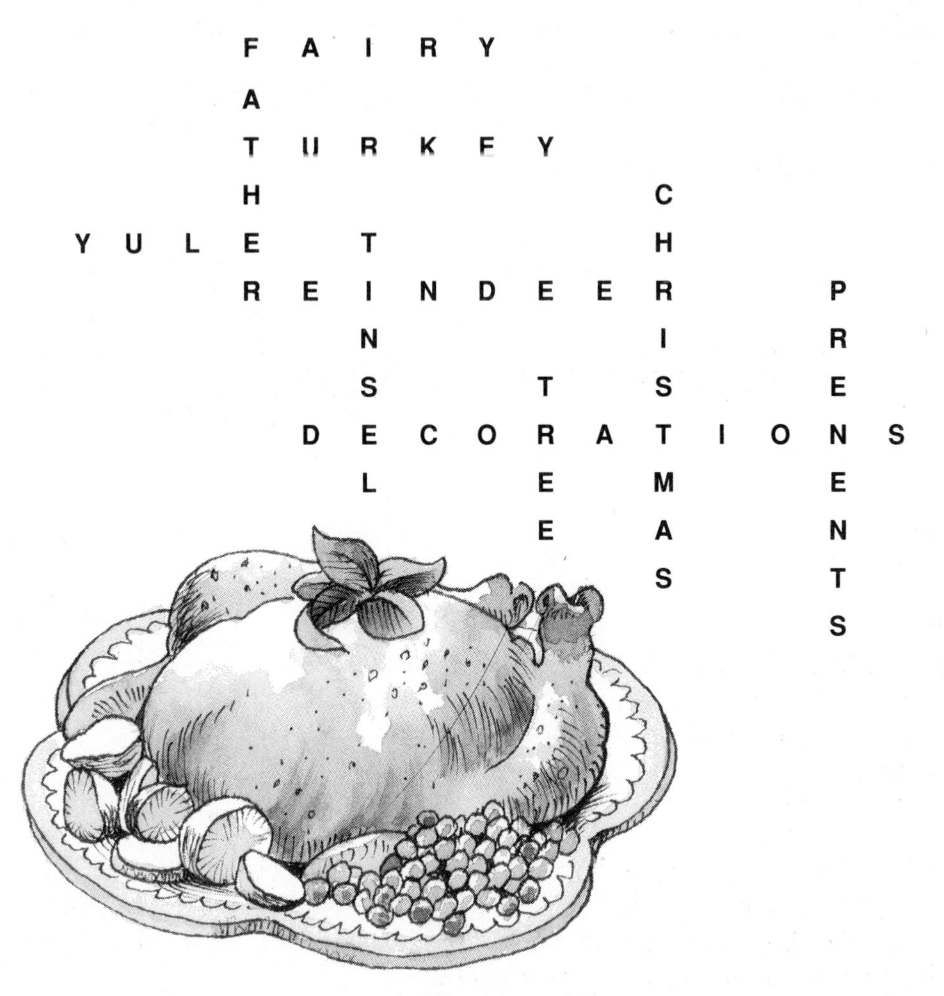


The game can either be played as individuals or as teams. To make it more competitive the winner is the person or team who gets the most Christmas words in the grid.

# Santa's journey

**Players**

Two to four.

**How to play**

Photocopy the game board below. The children will need a die and some counters to play and they will need to throw a six to start. The first player to arrive home again is the winner.

| | | | | | | |
|---|---|---|---|---|---|---|
| START 1 | No snow – miss a turn. 2 | 3 | 4 | Snowstorm – slide. 5 | 6 | 7 |
| Crash – go 30 back to 10. | 31 | 32 | 33 | 34 | Find Rudolph – 35 move on 8. | Reindeer hungry – 8 go back 4. |
| 29 | 52 | 53 | Genie gives you a wish 54 – move on 6. | 55 | 36 | 9 |
| 28 | 51 | 66 | 67 | 56 | 37 | 10 |
| Hurry on 6. 27 | 50 | 65 | 68 | 57 | Lost your way – 38 go back 2. | 11 |
| 26 | 49 | 64 | Fall asleep 69 – miss a go. | 58 | 39 | 12 |
| 25 | Running out of presents – 48 go back 3. | 63 | HOME 70 | 59 | 40 | Lucky square – 13 move on 6. |
| 24 | 47 | 62 | 61 | 60 | 41 | Unlucky square – 14 miss 2 turns. |
| Eating mince pies – 23 miss a turn. | 46 | 45 | 44 | Getting tired – sleep 43 through 2 turns. | 42 | 15 |
| 22 | 21 | Stuck in a chimney – 20 miss a turn. | 19 | 18 | 17 | 16 |

# Santa tangles

**Players**

Any number.

**How to play**

Ask the children to find the route that each Santa takes to go down the chimney.

# Picture-sound crossword

**Players**
Individuals.

**How to play**
Ask the children to complete the crossword shown below by taking the initial sound of each picture and transposing it to the corresponding squares of the blank grid.

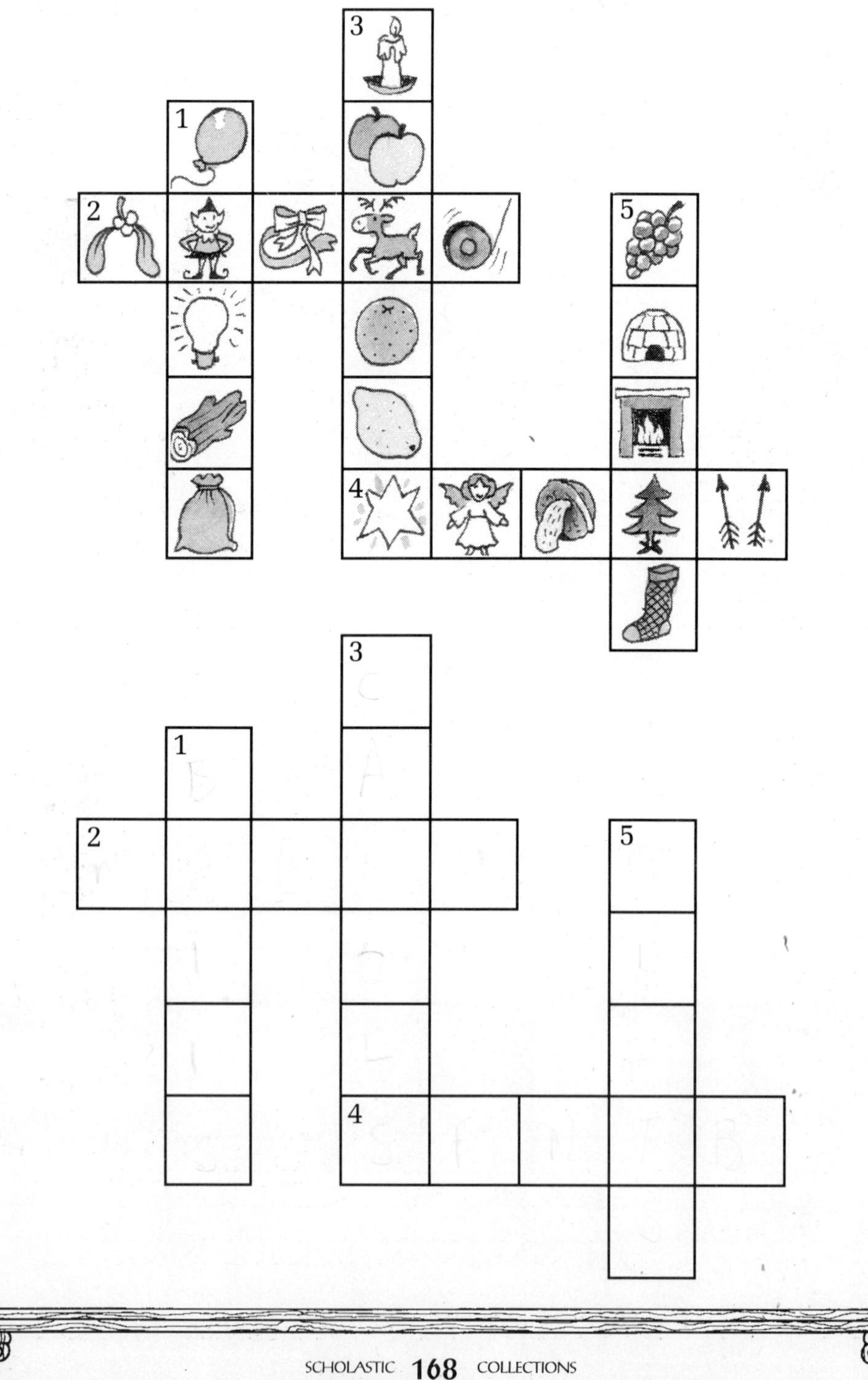

# Spot the difference

**Players**
Any number.

**How to play**
Ask the children to find ten differences between the two seemingly identical pictures. This can be made more competitive by adding a time limit. To cater for a larger group, divide the children up into teams giving points for speed and accuracy. The team with the most points wins.

# Stocking crossword

**Players**

Individuals.

**How to play**

Ask the children to solve the clues and fill in the answers on to the Christmas stocking.

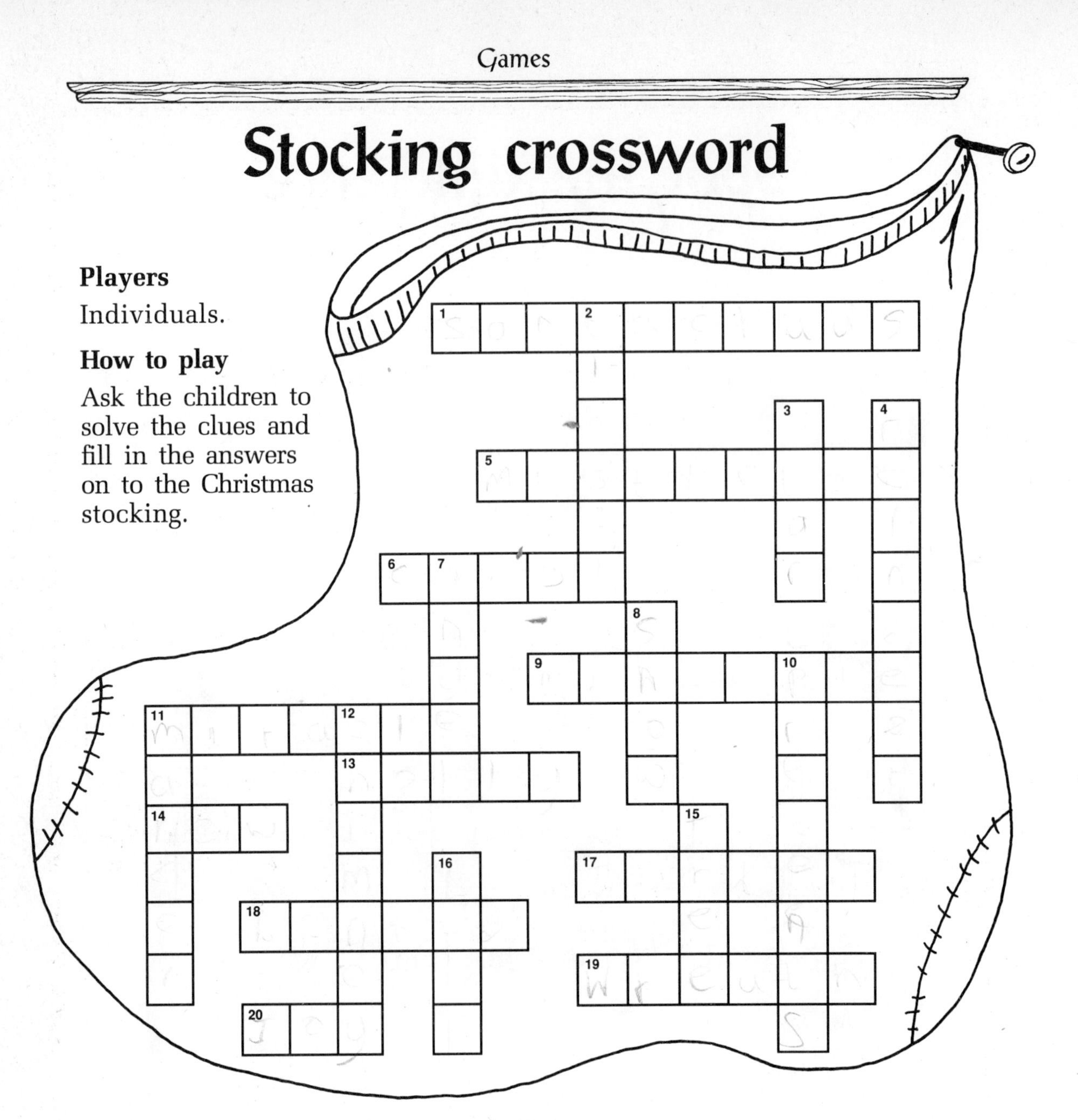

### Across

1. Father Christmas. (5,5)
5. You can kiss under it. (9)
6. A Christmas song. (5)
9. Leave one with a glass of sherry for Father Christmas, (5,3)
11. Jesus' birth was this. (7)
13. Prickly green leaves. (5)
14. __ born baby. (3)
17. Traditional Christmas fowl. (6)
18. Mary rode to Bethlehem on one. (6)
19. A decoration made of leaves to hang on the door. (6)
20. __ to the world! (3)

### Down

2. Silvery tree decoration. (6)
3. It shone above the stable. (4)
4. They pull Santa's sledge. (8)
7. A heavenly creature with wings. (5)
8. It makes a white Christmas. (4)
10. Things you give and receive at Christmas. (8)
11. Away in a ____. (6)
12. Santa comes down this. (7)
15. We decorate this at Christmas. (4)
16. You ring it. (4)

**Across** Santa Claus, Mistletoe, Carol, Mince pie, Miracle, Holly, New, Turkey, Donkey, Wreath, Joy
**Down** Tinsel, Star, Reindeer, Angel, Snow, Presents, Manger, Chimney, Tree, Bell

# THINGS TO MAKE

## Fun hats

**What you need**

Thin card, stapler, crêpe paper, tissue paper, adhesive, glitter, sugar paper, tin foil.

**What to do**

Measure the child's head and add on a further 5cm to the measurement. Cut out a rectangle from card to this size making sure it is about 10cm deep.

Let the children choose a colour of crepe paper and cut a length which will cover the card lengthwise but is 5cm deeper. Glue this on to the card and snip the excess crêpe paper so that it forms a fringe.

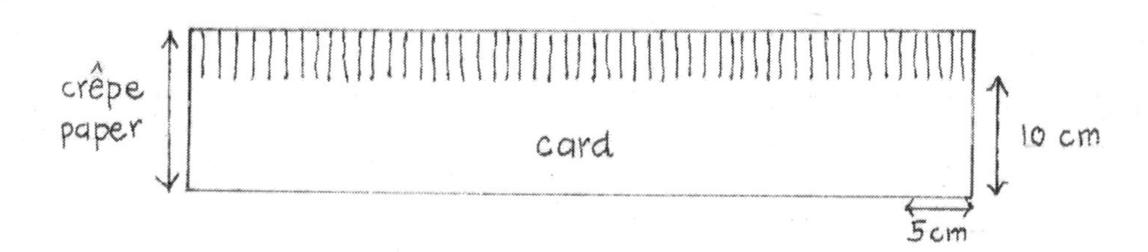


The children can decorate the crêpe paper using the tissue paper and tin foil. They can cut out stars, circles and triangles and stick these on to the hat band. When they have finished decorating, staple the two ends together, but making sure that it fits their heads easily.

To make the hat more interesting the children could use two layers of crêpe paper in contrasting colours so that the fringe is two or even three colours.

# Masks

### What you need

Thin card or hessian, scissors, sticky tape, stapler, fabric, adhesive.

### What to do

It is possible to use one basic mask shape as the basis for lots of different masks. Once the basic shape has been cut out from card the children can add to it to determine what the final mask will be. The children can cut out strips of card to go over and round the sides of their mask to keep them on. If these are stapled to the mask the staples should be covered with sticky tape so that they do not scratch. Ears can be stuck to the mask or on to a hair band which can be worn on the head with the mask.

Masks can be decorated with different fabrics and materials which can be glued on to the mask with PVA adhesive. Different materials can be used to achieve different effects. For example strips of fabric and brown paper can be used to make a lion's mane. Long strips can be used for the sides of the mane and short strips for the top.

For animals like a dog, a horse or a mouse you will need to add a long nose which can be stapled to the original mask shape. Again, cover the staples with sticky tape.

# Cone people

**What you need**

Thin card, tissue paper, cardboard tubes, compasses, cotton wool, pencil, scissors.

**What to do**

Ask the children to take a piece of thin card and draw a circle with a circumference of 10cm. They should cut the circle in half ensuring that the bottoms will fit snugly over the end of a cardboard tube.

Using crêpe paper the children can make outfits for the people and decorate the hats. They can make lots of different characters using the same basic bodies and just varying the decoration. Father Christmas, for example, can be made by covering the cardboard tube with red crêpe paper. This will form the face and body of the Father Christmas. Cover in red crêpe or tissue paper and decorate with cotton wool.

The hats should glued to the cardboard tubes and a face can be drawn on the tube.

Cone people can be used to form a three-dimensional display or as puppets (sticks can be taped inside the cone) for a Christmas assembly play.

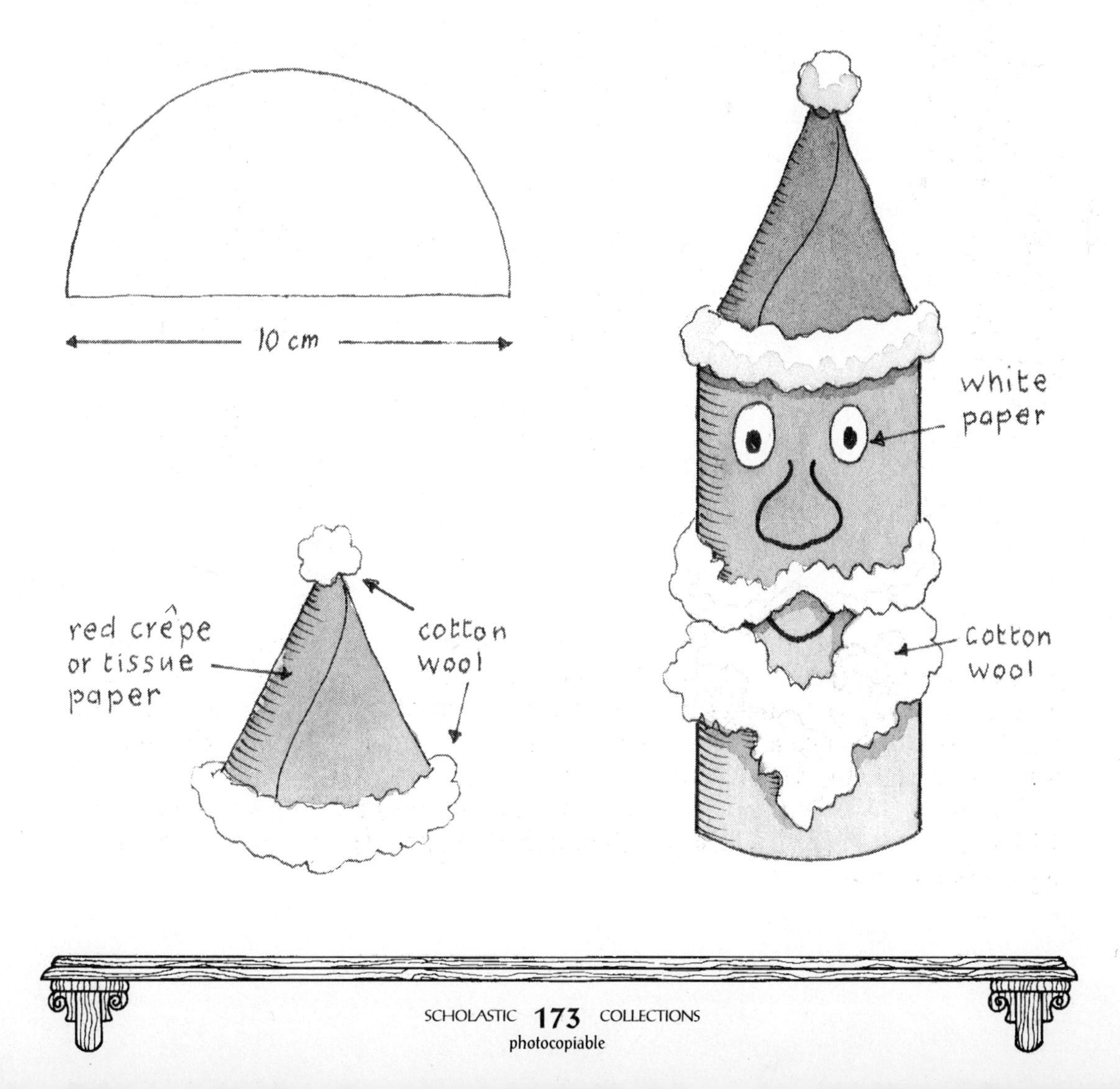

# Santa's reindeer

**What you need**

One and a half small cardboard tubes per child, brown paint, brushes, sticky tape or glue, corks or empty cotton reels, pipe cleaners, Plasticine.

**What to do**

Ask each child to paint one and a half cardboard tubes brown. When the paint has dried, have the child stick the pieces together to form the reindeer's head and body. Legs can be made from corks or cotton reels, and antlers from bended pipe cleaners. The child can add facial features using lumps of Plasticine.

# Ding dong bells

**What you need**

An egg carton, small yoghurt pots or paper cups, coloured ribbon, thread or wool, foil scraps or beads, paint, foil, coloured paper.

**What to do**

If the children are all using egg cartons they will need to cut out as many sections as they want bells. The bell shapes can then be painted or decorated with foil and coloured paper. For each bell shape the children should then take a bead or scrunched up piece of foil and thread it on to a long piece of thread, wool or ribbon. They can then make a hole in the top of each bell and thread the other end of the ribbon through. Tie three or four bells together, making a large bow. The bells can then be hung as an attractive decoration.

# Paper plate poinsettia

**What you need**

Paper plates, red paint, brushes, scissors, yellow felt, brass fasteners.

**What to do**

For each poinsettia the children should paint three paper plates red. When the paint has dried cut each plate into quarters, trimming one of the quarters into a petal shape. A small centre should then be cut from the yellow felt. The flower is assembled by inserting a brass fastener through an outside corner of the other pieces (which should be stacked first). The pieces can then be fanned out to form the blossom.

# Collapsible tree mobile

**What you need**

Green paper, different coloured rice paper, glitter, adhesive, decorative string or ribbon, scissors.

**What to do**

Ask the children to fold a square of green paper in half diagonally, and then in half again. They should place the paper so that the centre point is at the top and cut alternately from one side almost to the other until very near the top point. The paper should then be unfolded very carefully. Ornaments made out of different coloured paper and glitter can be glued or tied to the points of the tree, which can then be hung from the ceiling or on a display board.

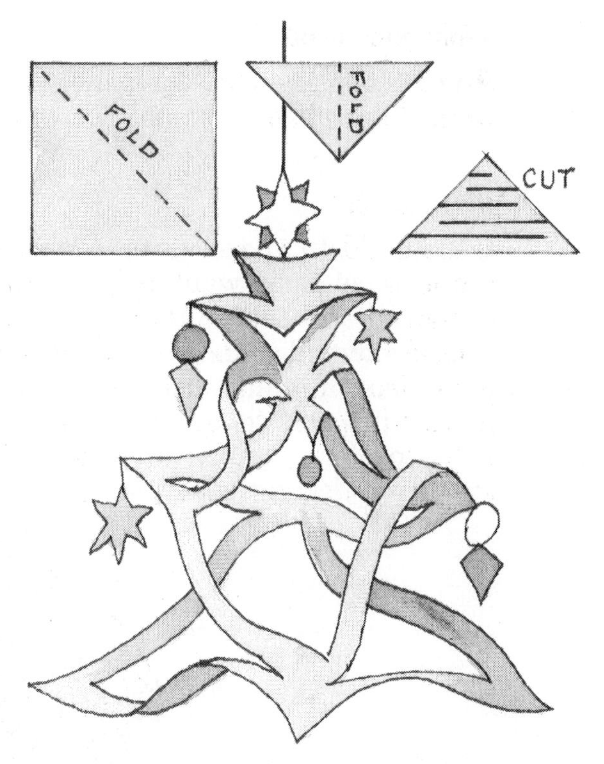

# Christmas star mobile

**What you need**

Several sheets of coloured foil paper, scissors, a pencil or knitting needle, adhesive, thread, dowelling or a wire coat-hanger.

**What to do**

Ask the children to cut out a circle from foil paper and fold it into eight equal sections. They should then draw a smaller circle around the centre.

Tell them to cut along each fold to the inner circle. Show them how to curl each edge of the paper, with a pencil or knitting needle, until it makes a point. They will need to fix each point with a dab of adhesive.

After several stars have been made in different colours, they should be suspended from threads of different lengths which can then be tied to a coathanger or piece of dowelling and hung from the ceiling.

# Circle bauble

**What you need**

Used Christmas cards, wallpaper scraps or coloured paper, pencils, scissors, a circle template (optional).

**What to do**

Ask each child to cut out nine circles from used Christmas cards, wallpaper scraps or coloured paper. She should then fold in half and cut eight of them as shown.

The eight folded and cut circles should be placed around the circumference of the ninth unfolded circle to form a bauble. The child can then punch a hole in the flat circle and thread a piece of wool or ribbon through it for hanging.

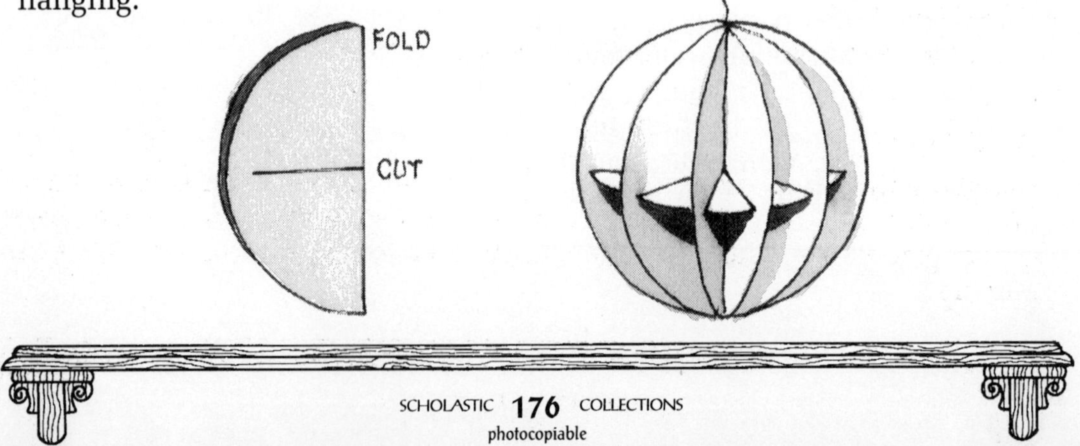

# Christmas banner

**What you need**

Large piece of heavy fabric, fabric scraps, scissors, dowelling, stapler, adhesive, string.

**What to do**

Staple one end of a large piece of fabric to a dowelling rod. Cut out a number of 30cm squares from the fabric scraps and ask the children to cut out Christmas shapes from other fabric scraps. They should glue one shape to each square, making sure that the shapes are glued on to squares of different colours. These squares can then be glued, in rows, on to the large piece of fabric.

Once the banner has dried tie string to each end of the dowelling and hang it from the ceiling.

# Paper gingerbread man

**What you need**

Brown paper, scissors, adhesive, cereal, buttons, small sweets.

**What to do**

Draw a large outline of a gingerbread man on brown paper and cut it out. The children can then glue circular-shaped cereals, buttons and small sweets on to the gingerbread man to make his features.

# Clip-on decorations

**What you need**

Paper, scissors, crayons, adhesive, wooden clothes peg.

**What to do**

Ask the children to draw, cut out and decorate different Christmas shapes from paper. They should then glue a wooden peg to the back of each shape and clip the shapes to the Christmas tree or to the ribbons on Christmas parcels.

# Pasta garland

**What you need**

Pasta tubes, shells or other shapes, paint, string or strong wool, glitter and adhesive.

**What to do**

Mix some glitter into some paint in a mixing tray. Do this with several different colour paints making sure you keep them apart. The children can then paint the pasta tubes with the glitter paints threading them with wool and hanging them up to dry. When all the tubes are dry the children can rearrange the different shapes and colour combinations and thread them on to clean wool. These garlands can then be used to decorate the Christmas tree.

As a variation, make pasta hanging chimes. Use long pasta twists or spirals for these. Tell the children to put a blob of adhesive inside each piece of pasta and attach a length of thread. These should be left to dry. The children can then gather a group of twists together, knot the threads at the top and paint the pasta with glitter paint.

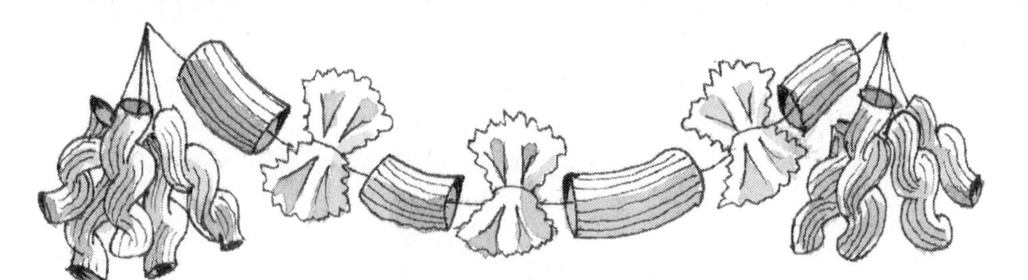

# Rag wreath

**What you need**

Strips of fabric and ribbon (about 15cm × 1cm), extra ribbon for bows, wire coat hanger.

**What to do**

Bend a wire coat hanger into a circle. Leave the hook on for hanging later. Let the children tie strips of fabric or ribbon around the wire until it is completely covered. Add bows at the top and sides as shown. Hang on the classroom door.

# Christingle

A tradition originating in Moravia is for children to receive a Christingle of Christmas Eve. This is an orange decorated with fruit and nuts, with a candle on top and a red ribbon around the middle. The orange represents the earth, the fruit and nuts remind us of the fruit of the earth, and the candle signifies Christ as the 'Light of the World'.

**What you need**

Oranges, candles, nuts, dates, raisins, cocktail sticks, red ribbon.

**What to do**

Show the children how to cut a piece of skin from the top of an orange and push a candle into it so that it is held firmly in place. They can then decorate the orange using fruit and nuts holding them in place with cocktail sticks. The christingle can then be finished off by tying a red ribbon around it.

These candles can be used in the school carol service. The children can process through the audience during the singing of the carols with the candles alight and the lights turned down low or out. At the end of the carols all the candles would be blown out at the same time and the service ended.

# Sweet parcels

**What you need**

Christmas wrapping paper, scissors, adhesive, tinsel, glitter, ribbon, small sweets, old matchboxes, tissue paper.

**What to do**

Tell each child to take a small matchbox and some Christmas paper. They should put a small amount of tissue paper inside the matchbox and fill it with small sweets such as Dolly Mixtures. They can then wrap the matchbox up in the Christmas paper so that it looks like a small parcel.

The finished parcel can then be tied round with gold or silver thread and hung from the Christmas tree with a wool or thread loop. The children can also decorate these small parcels with tinsel if they like.

# Animal bookmarks

**What you need**

Thin card, felt-tipped pens or crayons, old greetings cards, wrapping paper or fabric scraps, coloured wool.

**What to do**

The children can either cut out an animal's head from an old card, or make their own out of card and scrap materials.

They should then plait or knot together coloured wool and attach the plait to the back of the animal's head. The 'tail' of the bookmark will lie inside the pages of the book and the head will peep over the top.

# Father Christmas string holder

**What you need**

A large cylindrical container (for example, empty drinking chocolate container), coloured felt-tipped pens, coloured paper, scissors, sticky tape or adhesive, ball of string, brass fasteners.

**What to do**

Start with a cylindrical container to make this useful gift. The children can use different coloured paper and felt-tipped pens to make the container into a Father Christmas figure (or any character of their choice). Use the lid of the container as the base of a hat which can be taken off and replaced as needed. The children should make a hole in the side of the container large enough for the string to come through and should fix a paper fastener to it to hold the end of the string in place. They could give Father Christmas a 'sack' in which to keep handy a small pair of scissors for cutting the string.

# Festive napkin rings

**What you need**

Small cardboard tubes, different coloured wool, different coloured paper, coloured felt-tipped pens, scissors, adhesive.

**What to do**

Let the children cut cardboard tubes into 2.5cm rings. The rings can then be painted with adhesive and wrapped round with coloured wool. If the children wish they can add a festive motif made from coloured paper (for example, holly leaves and berries, a snowman) or perhaps decorate them with the initials of family members so they each have their own napkin ring.

# Tiered dish

**What you need**

Paper plates of two different sizes, pipe cleaners, empty cotton reels, adhesive, materials for decorating dish.

**What to do**

This dish makes a useful gift. Ask the children to make a small hole in the centre of a large paper plate and a smaller one. They should then glue an empty cotton reel over the holes as shown and thread a pipe cleaner through to form a handle. The children can then use their imaginations to decorate the dish.

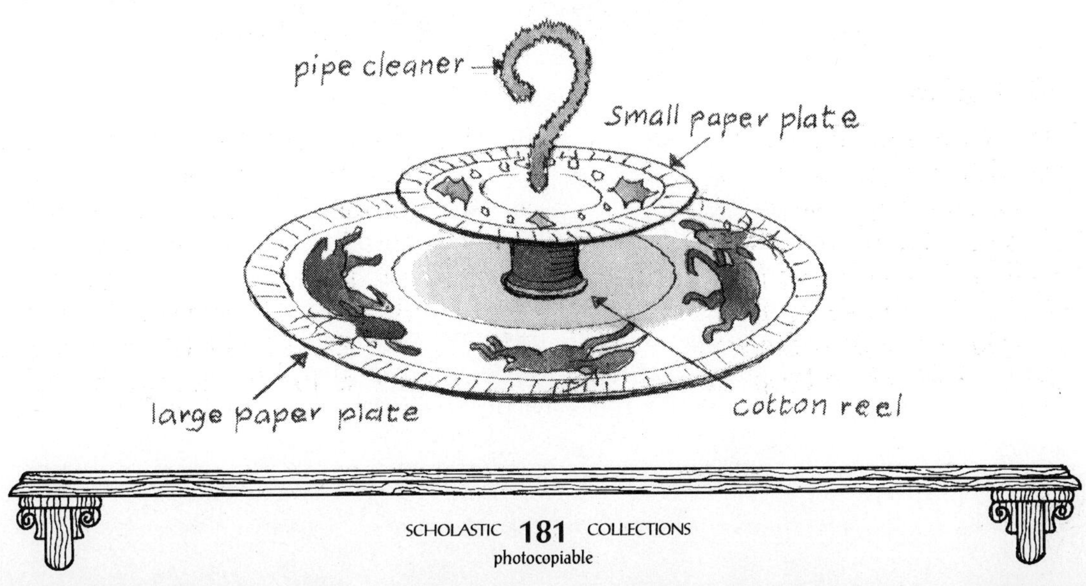

# Party place-mats

**What you need**

30cm × 45cm pieces of card, red and brown paper, felt-tipped pens, ribbons, scissors, adhesive.

**What to do**

Cut out rectangular pieces of red paper so that they are slightly smaller than the card and let the children cut round them to make scalloped edges. Ask the children to glue these on to the card and then glue two strips of ribbon on to the paper in the shape of a cross.

Cut out gingerbread men from brown paper and let the children decorate and write their names on them and then stick them in the centre of the mats.

# Frosted pictures

**What you need**

Old Christmas cards, cardboard, PVA adhesive, water, Epsom salts, brushes.

**What to do**

Ask the children to cut out Christmas pictures and mount them on to cardboard. They should then dilute PVA adhesive with an equal amount of water and brush over their pictures with this solution. While the pictures are drying, make a salt solution by stirring Epsom salts into warm water until the salt will no longer dissolve. Once the glue solution has dried the children can brush the salt solution on to the areas of their pictures where they require a frosted effect and wait for the solution to dry.

# Christmas postcards

**What you need**

Card, felt-tipped pens.

**What to do**

Ask the children to cut out postcard shapes from card. They can then draw a Christmas picture on one side of the card and a vertical line down the middle of the other side. They can write a Christmas message on the left-hand side, the address of the receiver on the other side and post them!

# Bear hug Christmas card

**What you need**

Thin card, scissors, felt-tipped pens or crayons, ribbon.

**What to do**

Give the children a bear template to draw around. They should then cut out the shape and draw in the pads and claws. Show them how to fold the arms, legs and head forwards along the dotted lines so that they overlap.

Using felt-tipped pens or crayons, they can draw on the facial features, and then attach a bow to the head.

When the bear is complete, open up the card and let the children write a Christmas message inside.

# Christmas tree card

**What you need**

Thin card 24cm × 18cm, wool, large needle.

**What to do**

Tell the children to fold the card in half so that they have a card measuring 12cm × 18cm. They should then use a pencil and ruler to draw an outline of a Christmas tree on the front and mark dots at 1cm intervals along the outline. Ask the children to use a needle to make a hole on each dot and rub out the pencil lines.

Using green thread the children can join up the branches of the tree and then use brown thread for the pot. This is a very simple technique, but is also very effective.

# Embroidered card

**What you need**

Thin card 27cm × 13cm, binca 7cm × 7cm, wool, large embroidery needle.

**What to do**

Let the children embroider a Christmas shape in the centre of the binca using coloured wool and simple stitches such as cross stitch.

Tell them to mark out the card into three equal sections each measuring 9cm × 13cm and to cut a rectangular window in the first section that is big enough for the design to show through. They should then stick the binca with sticky tape or adhesive so that the picture faces out.

Show them how to fold the card as follows: Fold section A back and glue it to the back of section B. Then fold section C towards section B. The children can then turn the card over, open it and write their message inside.

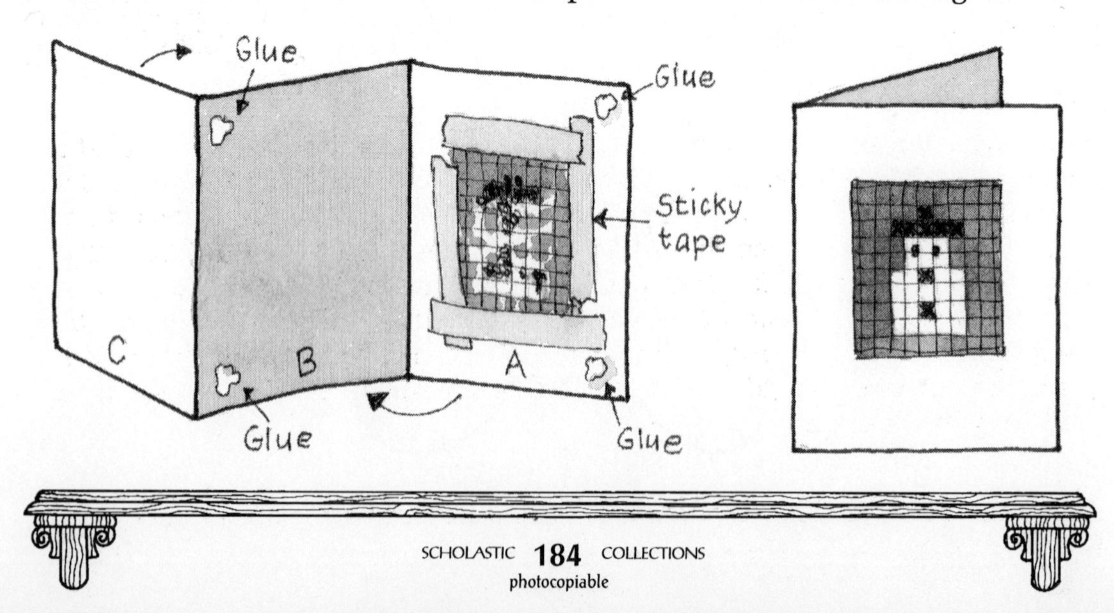

# Snowflake card

**What you need**

Thin coloured card (approximately 24cm × 18cm), white paper, compasses, pencil, scissors, adhesive, ruler.

**What to do**

Tell the children to fold the coloured card in half to make a card shape and then to draw a circle 9cm to 10cm diameter on the card ensuring that part of the circle overlaps the fold.

The children can cut out the circle shape but they must not cut around the fold.

Ask them to draw another circle on a piece of white paper, but making sure that it is slightly smaller than the diameter of the card. They should then fold this circle into four and cut out different shapes.

They can then open out their snowflakes and glue them carefully to the cards. The children can make up a rhyme for the inside and making sure the fold is at the top, cut a straight bit off the bottom so that the card will stand up properly.

# Pop-up card

**What you need**

An A4 sheet of paper or thin card, coloured paper or old Christmas cards, felt-tipped pens or crayons, scissors.

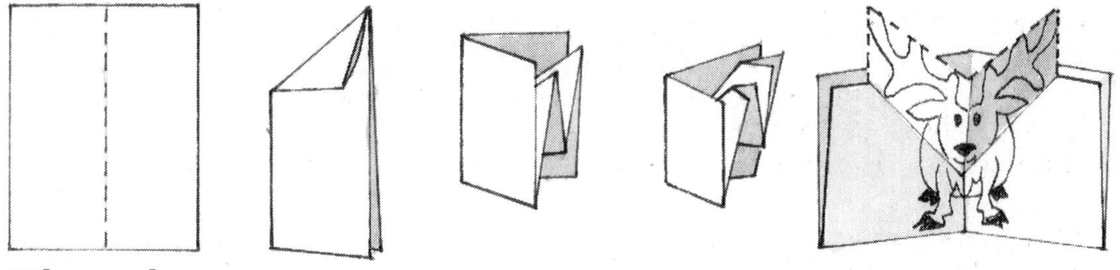

**What to do**

Show the children how to make the basic pop-up card as follows: fold the paper in half length ways. Keeping the fold on the left, fold the top corner from the centre fold to the edge. Next, fold the same corner backwards to make a good crease. Open the paper out again and fold the in half the other way. Close the card along the first fold, pulling out the middle section as you do so. Cut off the top edge of the card. When it is opened again, the middle section will pop up. The card is now ready to decorate either with a picture cut from an old Christmas card or one made from coloured paper and crayons.

# A chocolate log

**What you need**

18 plain sweet biscuits, small pot of double cream, one teaspoon of cocoa powder, one teaspoon of icing sugar, a basin, a whisk, a knife and fork, a plate, silver foil.

**What to do**

Put the cream, sugar and cocoa in the basin. Whisk them until the mixture is just stiff enough to stand in peaks. Spread half the mixture on the biscuits and sandwich them together in a long roll. Wrap the roll of biscuits in foil and put it in the fridge with the rest of the mixture. After two hours unwrap the roll and put it on the plate. Cover it with the rest of the mixture. Drag the fork over the surface to make it look like the bark of a tree.

# Macaroons

**What you need**

250g caster sugar, 150g almonds, 1 tablespoon rice flour, 2 egg whites, rice paper, 25 split almonds, two basins, a wooden spoon, a whisk, a baking tray.

**What to do**

Mix the sugar, almonds and rice flour in a basin and set to one side. Beat the egg whites lightly in another basin. Add the dry ingredients and beat to a smooth firm consistency. Leave to stand for five minutes then roll into small balls and place slightly apart on a baking tray lined with rice paper. Flatten slightly and place a split almond on each one. Bake in a preheated oven 180°C or Gas Mark 4 for 20 minutes.

# Marshmallow snowmen

**What you need**

Marshmallows, licorice ribbon, hard gums, assorted small sweets, a small amount of white icing, cocktail sticks.

**What to do**

For each snowman you will need three marshmallows and two cocktail sticks. Attach two marshmallows together with a cocktail stick and place a hard gum on top for a hat. Cut the other marshmallows in half and use them for arms, attaching them to the main body with the second cocktail stick. Use the icing sugar as 'glue' to decorate the snowmen.

# Sponge snowmen

**What you need**

100g flour, 4 eggs, 100g castor sugar, 100g butter or soft margarine melted, few drops vanilla essence, jam, heated and sifted, desiccated coconut, glacé cherries, peel, oven and hob, whisk, wooden spoon, individual dariole moulds, saucepans, sieve, bowls, scales.

**What to do**

Tell the children to sieve the flour and set aside. They should then warm the eggs and sugar and whisk them together until they are thick and creamy. They should then fold the flour very lightly into the egg mixture, followed by the melted butter and vanilla essence. They should then pour the mixture in to moulds and cook near the top of a moderate oven at 200°C or gas mark 6 for 10 to 15 minutes. Once the mixture has been cooked the children should turn the sponges out to cool and when they are completely cold, brush them with jam and roll them in coconut. The children can add buttons, eyes and other features using candied peel and cherries.

# Snowballs

**What you need**

50g butter, 100g icing sugar, 1 tablespoon drinking chocolate, desiccated coconut, a mixing bowl, a wooden spoon.

**What to do**

Beat the butter and icing sugar together, then mix in one tablespoon of drinking chocolate. Form the mixture into small balls and roll each one in desiccated coconut.

# Chocolate truffles

**What you need**

100g butter, 100g icing sugar, 50g cocoa powder, 4-6 tablespoons desiccated coconut, 1 cup chopped dates and raisins, vanilla essence, chocolate vermicelli, a mixing bowl, a wooden spoon.

**What to do**

Cream the butter and sugar together. Add the other ingredients and mix them together thoroughly. Leave the mixture to stand for half an hour, then roll it in to balls and dip them in chocolate vermicelli.

# Christmas sweet container

**What you need**

A small box, Christmas wrapping paper or scrap materials, scissors, adhesive, cling film, silver foil.

**What to do**

The children can decorate their boxes with wrapping paper or scrap materials. Before placing their sweets in the box they should line the bottom with silver foil. The cling film can be used to cover the box, protecting the sweets, but allowing them to be seen.

# Index

# Acknowledgements

**The publishers gratefully acknowledge permission to reproduce the following copyright material:**

**Poetry**

© 1992 Moira Andrew for 'Christmas past' and 'What did you have for Christmas?'; © 1992 Robert Brown and Greg Shepherd for 'Christmas poem'; © 1992 Ann Bryant for 'Crackers', 'Snowman', 'Tapping' and 'Tidy up for Christmas'; © 1992 Rebecca Byrne for 'Christmas is here'; © 1992 Sarah Copeland for 'The colours of Christmas'; © 1987 Pie Corbett for 'Scarecrow Christmas'; © 1992 John Cotton for 'A week to Christmas' and 'Christmas riddles'; © 1992 Katie Eastman for 'The cook sees the stable'; © 1992 Eileen Gladston for 'Christmas', 'The snowman' and 'Tom's up the tree'; © 1992 Amy Iversen for 'Christmas night'; © 1992 Wes Magee for 'Christmas haikus', 'It's Christmas', 'It's Christmas Eve', 'Questions on Christmas Eve' and 'The school field in December'; Walker Books for 'Santa Claus is Superman' by Colin McNaughton (1988); © 1992 David Minks for 'Once there was a cold country'; © 1992 Brian Moses for 'Christmas day', 'Christmas Eve' and 'Dear Santa'; © 1992 Adam Nuckley for 'I mustn't go to sleep'; © 1987 John Rice for 'A gift from the stars'; Scholastic Canada Ltd for 'The present' © 1983 Mary Blakeslee; © Scholastic Publications, Inc. for 'Bundles' by John Farrar and 'Santa Claus and company' by LaVonne Guenther; © 1992 Daniel Sedgwick for 'Christmas Eve'; © 1992 Fred Sedgwick for 'Once there was a shepherd' and 'Winter song'; © 1992 Ian Souter for 'Our family Christmas' and 'Our family's taking back Christmas shopping list'; © 1992 Benedict Taylor for 'Christmas morn'; © 1990 Charles Thompson for 'Christmas'; © 1992 Rosemary Crabb Wyke for 'In a dark wood'.

**Stories**

© 1992 Ann Bryant for 'Shake, rattle and roll'; © 1992 John Cotton for 'Christmas in the 1930's'; Faber and Faber for 'Christmas Day' from *The Country Child* by Alison Uttley; Harper Collins Publications for 'The Great Christmas Mix-up' by Elizabeth Laird from *Big Beans or Little Beans* (1991) compiled by Julia Eccleshare; Mark Paterson and Associates for 'Seven shopping days to Christmas' from *Grimble and Grimble at Christmas* by Clement Freud (Puffin); Murray Pollinger for 'A Troublesome Year for Father Christmas' by Sally Grindley from *Christmas Stories for the Very Young* (Kingfisher Books Ltd, 1990); Octopus Publishing Group for extract from 'Images in Bethlehem' from *A Web of Stories* by Grace Hallworth (Methuen Children's Books, 1990); Scholastic Publications, Inc. for 'Alfred's shoes' by Annabelle Sumera, 'Henry's Christmas ear-muffs' and 'Mrs Christmas and the sleeping polar bear' by Frances B. Watts from *Instructor's Read-aloud Anthology*; © 1992 Ian Souter for 'Who needs Superman?'; © 1992 C. Walsh for 'Bedding down for winter'; © 1979 David Henry Wilson for 'Father Christmas and Father Christmas' from *Getting Rich with Jeremy James* (Chatto & Windus).

**Plays**

© 1992 Ann Bryant for 'Is it true?', 'Lord of the dance' and 'The magic Christmas logs'; © 1990 Lynn Dolby for 'Quick Christmas performances'; © 1992 Robert Duncan for 'The Christmas birthday'; © 1989 Diana Jones for 'A boy is born'; © 1992 Wes Magee for 'The master of the time vortex and his magic Christmas show'; © 1991 Rosalia Makinson for 'Five little fir trees'; Scholastic Publications, Inc. for 'The smallest Christmas tree' by Winifred B. Cooper.

**Songs**

© 1992 Ann Bryant for 'Angel song', 'Animal song', 'Greedylumps' exercise song', 'Grumpydumps' work piece', 'I danced in the morning' (words only), 'Is it true?', 'Kings' and Queens' song' and 'Lazyslumps' song'; © 1989 Debbie Campbell for 'Do you believe in Father Christmas?'; © 1963 Sydney Carter for 'I danced in the morning' (music only); © 1983 Elizabeth Chapman for 'Sleep little baby' (words only); © 1992 Mike Fenton for 'I wonder how it was' (words only); © 1983 Peter Morrell for 'Sleep little baby' (music only); © David Moses for 'Jesus was a baby in Bethlehem' (1983) and 'Paper chains' (1992); © 1990 Gillian Parker for 'Merry Christmas'.

Every effort has been made to trace copyright holders. The publishers apologise for any inadvertent omissions.